THE TREATMENT YOU DESERVE

The Right Way To Get It From The New NHS

Dr Iain Robertson-Steel
with Chris Vaughan

RIGHT WAY

Typeset in 11/12pt Times by One & A Half Graphics, Redhill, Surrey. Printed and bound in Great Britain by Cox & Wyman Ltd., Reading, Berkshire.

The *Right Way* series and the *Paperfronts* series are both published by Elliot Right Way Books, Brighton Road, Lower Kingswood, Tadworth, Surrey, KT20 6TD, U.K.

CONTENTS

Introduction

Not a day passes without a story in the news telling of failure somewhere in our National Health Service: operations cancelled and patients sent home, patients with serious conditions waiting too long for treatments, wards closed because of staff shortage — a catalogue implying crisis if not impending catastrophe.

Since it began about fifty years ago, the National Health Service has been a source of British pride. It has been the only network in the land touching every social class, the only system nurturing the populace from conception to burial. And yet its foundations were faulty.

From the perspective of the 1940's and in a Europe devastated by war, it seemed that once the current maladies of the nation had been dealt with, the demands on the service would subside and a rudimentary insurance system could pay for it. The concept was that if you cured extreme illness the population would become healthier, less healthcare would be needed and the demand would drop. In retrospect we know that this was a plan mainly designed to combat early death in the form of infectious diseases and birth complications, and very successful it was.

What we can now see is that this approach, allied with better housing, better sanitation and better nutrition, increased survival and general life expectancy so that the population became vulnerable to all the other ills to which flesh is heir. The early killers such as bronchitis, pneumonia and infectious diseases were substantially diminished, only to be replaced by other more demanding diseases such as cancer and heart attack later on in an extended life cycle. The treatments, too, became progressively more complex and expensive as medicine absorbed the scientific breakthroughs of the twentieth century.

The health service today has to cope with much more than its founding fathers envisaged. They did not foresee an aging population and a relative reduction in tax revenue or an increase in the cost of medical technology and treatment. Nor did they foresee that the more you offer people, the more they expect. Accordingly they constructed a centrally funded system that would pay for any health demand made upon it. Which meant that until very recently we expected the state to provide whatever treatment we needed when we needed it, even if there was a wait.

Rationing And The Internal Market

Not any more. To judge by the reforms Parliament has enacted, the Government has obviously decided that it, and you the taxpayer, cannot continue to pay for the health service in its traditional form. It has fundamentally, and covertly, changed the health service. From now on its resources will be limited and treatment will be rationed.

The new legislation has turned the service into an internal market where, in the words of the Health Minister, "The money follows the patient". By separating the users (the Health Authorities and large GP practices) from the providers (the hospitals), the Government has made it a service that is pre-eminently cost-conscious and competitive. The users are now urged to shop around and look for the best deal from the providers.

As a potential customer (new terminology) or ill person (old terminology) in this new environment, you will need to know what and where resources are available and how to compete for them. This book will show you how. It will give you a strategy for getting the best out of the service for your family and those for whom you care. The strategy will differ, depending on what your needs are. Whether, for instance, you are a young woman facing her first pregnancy, or a parent with young children or a middle aged person with responsibility for elderly relatives, your demands will change accordingly. This book will show you how to focus those demands, how to target them and how to achieve the outcome you want.

You should be in no way deterred by the current emphasis on rationing and cost-cutting from asking for the best treatment available to you. Our health service has been established and grown through the tax contributions of our parents and grandparents and now, in turn, is being maintained by us. The politicians and economists say it is "free at the point of use" but this is a shorthand way of saying that our treatment is being paid for from the common purse to which we have all contributed, rather than coming directly out of our own pocket. The NHS has never been "free". It may be that you have treatment or care that exceeds your personal contribution but on the other hand you may go through life relatively free from illness. We cannot predict what lies in store, but it is the mark of a civilised society that adequate provision is made for its sick and weak members, who, so long as they have a responsible and informed attitude towards seeking professional help, have every right to proper medical treatment. Remember each individual pays annually more than £600 to the NHS in direct and indirect taxation, or each family approximately £1500 per annum.

This is a practical book. It takes the system as it now is and guides you through it. Although it necessarily touches upon the politics and philosophy of universal healthcare and is aware of these issues, it principally takes the reality of the new system and tells you how to survive by showing how it can be used to get the treatment that is best for you.

1.

What Has Changed?

Whatever plans you have for yourself, whatever your hopes and aspirations and however you formulate the personal goal called happiness, they will all come to nothing if you do not enjoy good health and if you cannot remedy or avoid the illnesses that come your way. Since the personal and financial consequences of long-term illness are so shattering, good health must not be taken for granted.

In most societies good health is not something that people take for granted and in our own society illness and early death were commonplace until the late nineteen forties. Most people living in Britain today, however, have grown up with the benefits of the National Health Service and take good health and freely available treatment as a right. Making separate provision for these does not figure in most people's plans. The state has traditionally dealt with universal healthcare and, on the whole, has done so satisfactorily. The Government now wants more accountability and better value for money introduced into the system and therefore certain GPs will have budgets, and hospitals will compete with each other for the patients that the GPs refer and pay for out of these budgets.

If you have a GP who is a fundholder and runs out of budget or who is a non-fundholder and does not have access to a budget, or if you have an illness that is costly to treat or non-urgent, you could find diagnosis and treatment being postponed or delayed to such an extent that it plays havoc with your ability to work and consequently with your life. Therefore it is essential that people once again start to take active steps to secure their health and health provision if they wish to realise their goals in life. This book will show you how to do that within the new system without having to have recourse to inadequate private insurance or perhaps even dangerous patent remedies.

You can maximise your chances of getting the best treatment and healthcare if you are familiar with the reforms that have been introduced recently and with the new system that has resulted, if, that is, you understand the new rules of the game. Before explaining what these are and how to work them to your advantage it is essential to list the demands a person is likely to make on medical services in the course of a lifetime. In this way not only will you be able to anticipate your own need for medical intervention at each lifestage but you will be in a position to do so for the members of your family, both young and elderly. Moreover, you will be able to see that, because we live longer than previous generations, we need to get used to the idea of having the support of the latest medical facilities and knowledge if we are to continue to lead useful and productive lives.

The First Five Years

At the start of the life cycle and for the first five years the health service makes a great effort to ensure that our children are fit and healthy. From the point of view that dominates all health discussion today — the economic point of view — this makes good sense. A concern to put things right early on and prevent avoidable disease saves resources later.

Once the mother becomes aware she is pregnant she will receive screening from her GP along with referral to a midwife and to the hospital where the foetus will be checked for abnormalities. She will be given health advice and encouraged to take vitamin and folic acid supplements, if this has not already been started by her GP. The hospital will take every effort to deliver the baby safely once it is due and if a normal delivery is not feasible then assisted delivery will be carried out either by forceps or by caesarean method. A UK mortality rate of seven deaths per one thousand births is good but not among the three best in the world. The variation across the country and even between hospitals in the same locality should make us aware that it is never too soon to start thinking about health risks and life chances. Some premature babies will receive intensive care until they are able to be nursed by their mothers, but others in under-resourced areas of the country will not be so lucky. Whether babies of extremely low birth-weight, less than 500 grams, who take up a disproportionate amount of resources, should be treated at all, is currently a matter of debate.

Practical Points
Early ante-natal care. Early ante-natal screening. Healthy diet. Good GP. Good midwife. Don't smoke. Use the resources available to you.

If the baby is healthy, the mother will be allowed home and will be supervised by a midwife for the first ten days, and a full vaccination and immunisation programme will be started by the GP with developmental checks taking place periodically over the first five years of the child's life. Health visitors may also be asked to play a role in the early support given to mother and child, but the Government is beginning to cut back on this service. Care in the Community needs a strong, well-staffed Primary Healthcare Team, that is, enough GPs and support staff.

Practical Points
Make sure the baby is immunised. Use health checks. Use health visitor. Use GP.

Childhood
If the years of toddlerhood are managed properly then childhood (5–11 yrs) should involve less medical intervention. The child will be immunised against the major childhood diseases, except chicken pox, and should suffer only the winter bugs that get passed around at school. The main causes of death for children of this age are accidents (900 every year and another 10,000 permanently disabled, boys being the main victims); and malignancies such as leukaemia.

Practical Points
Take precautions: on the road — car seat belts, and safety helmets and reflective gear for bikes, and at home: safe play — prevent falls, burns and poisoning — smoke alarms, safety gates, power socket guards.

Adolescence
Accidents, again, are the main cause of death in adolescents but drug taking and sex enter the picture now, with their attendant threats to health such as AIDS and hepatitis B. Healthcare and health promotion for adolescents is to my mind inadequate. A lot more could be done officially to educate and inform young people about the hazards of drug, alcohol and substance abuse, about healthy eating and an active lifestyle. This is the age when habits are formed

that will carry them forward into their adult years. Parents have a responsibility but a lot more effort could be made via schools and the mass media to back up parental guidance. The lessons of safe sex need to be learnt but without losing sight of sex as a natural and enjoyable activity.

Practical Points
Be aware of the current pressures of adolescent life − drink, drugs and unprotected sex. Education in road safety.

Young Adulthood
Too many young adults (18−24 yrs) die or are injured in our society in road traffic accidents. In my years working in Accident and Emergency, I have had first hand experience dealing with the unnecessary carnage of road traffic accidents. The greatest proportion of the head and limb injuries I see are sustained by young men under the age of 24; alcohol is frequently involved. National statistics bear this out. Drink-driving, however, is a problem of many in mid-life. For instance, contrary to the popular view, Summer and not Christmas is the greatest period for drink-driving, and it is the middle-aged and not the young who are the main culprits here.

As we shall show, health is not just a question of preventing or curing disease; it means truly appreciating the risks inherent in our way of life and managing them appropriately. As far as motor transport is concerned, we, as a society, have an irrational blind-spot. We accept a lower level of safety than we do with any other area of activity and are prepared to tolerate, year after year, a huge toll of death and serious injury without taking sufficient action to diminish it. If the same number of people who die each year on the roads (3,800 men, women and children [1993]) died altogether in a single natural catastrophe, not only would the nation be in mourning for weeks, but prompt action would be taken to ensure it never occurred again. In addition to the deaths there is an enormous amount of morbidity (long-term consequences) which affect people for life.

Mid-life
In mid-life (36−65) those two great killers in our society, cardiovascular disease and cancer, tend increasingly to manifest themselves. Cardiovascular disease is, on the whole, a disease of modern life. Sedentary lifestyle and a lack of exercise, combined with smoking and alcohol and a poor diet, take their toll, usually resulting in narrowing of the coronary arteries. Heart disease affects

men more than women, particularly before the menopause, due to physiological differences. Women in mid-life are prone to cancer of the cervix, the breast and the ovaries. Men have an increased risk of testicular cancer in young adulthood, of bowel cancer in mid-life and prostatic cancer in later life. It is worth pointing out here that a competent GP should be able to detect the early signs of these diseases and take appropriate action. The development of cost-effective screening programmes and the use of them by those at risk, is essential. In terms of screening, men are currently disadvantaged compared with women.

*Practical Points
Stop smoking and reduce your coronary disease and stroke risk and add years to your life. (N.B. Doctors have many other problems, but very few smoke!) Attend for regular screening, e.g. cervical smears, breast screening and blood pressure checks. If checks are not offered, ask for them, the Patient's Charter For General Practice says you can. (See Chapter 8.)

Mid-life is also when certain body parts begin to malfunction or wear out and surgery may be increasingly called for. Hernias occur, cartilages in the knee need to be trimmed, repaired or removed, and joints wear out. It is in mid-life, too, when for women the after-effects of child-birth, such as urinary incontinence, begin to surface. Gall stones and kidney stones start to make themselves felt, in both sexes. Interestingly, insurance statistics reflect the fact that women live longer, sicker lives.

The Third Age
Many of us will reach retirement at 65, fit and well, looking forward to enjoying our ten "reward years" in good health, adequately financed and planned for.

Old Age
Finally and inevitably, there comes the stage in the latter years of our life when our illnesses become chronic and incurable, requiring long-term management and alleviation. Diabetes, rheumatism, cancer, angina, coronary artery disease, joint disease, and senile dementia, are amongst such diseases typical of old age. The average sixty five year old, it is said, has six active disease processes. Hopefully, with adequate care, we can enjoy the 65–75 years period as a happy and fruitful one.

If you are a man living in the late twentieth century you will have a life expectancy of 75 years. If you are a woman it will be 85 years. The longer you live, the more chance there is of you becoming totally incapable either physically or mentally, suffering from dementia and/or incontinence and requiring full-time care and being unable to manage your own affairs and live an independent life. Interestingly, on average, by the time a man reaches 75, his children will be in their 50's, and when a woman reaches 85, her children will be potential pensioners.

In case you feel at this point that I am being unduly gloomy or pessimistic, I hasten to add that I am talking here about probabilities. This book is not about minimal survival but living healthily with a good quality of life. It will show you how to take good care of yourself using the resources provided by the state, not just for tackling illness when it occurs but for tapping into its storehouse of medical knowledge so that the typical complaints that are prevalent at each stage of life can be avoided or dealt with quickly and without fuss.

Overall, the system the Government has devised for dealing with the nation's diseases is strong in some areas, weak in others. It is strong at the beginning of our life cycle, weak in dealing with the problems of old age and mental illness. Strong in dealing with the routine, quick, remedies, weak in handling the rare, unusual and long-term illnesses.

Because the Government has reformed the health service along competitive lines, hospitals may only be keen to treat those cases that bring a quick profit such as ear, nose and throat surgery, simple gynaecological procedures, hernia repair and hip replacement: simple items of service jobs that are easily identified and quickly done: high earners but low users of resources.

An apparent weakness of the new system is that, on the whole, it lacks resources in the area of chronic illness, both physical and mental, and in the care of the aged. It is early days yet and we will have to see what happens in practice but the signs so far are not encouraging. The Government is increasingly directing care to the community, to already hard-pressed and overstretched community and general practitioner services. The Government has a stated policy to increase day care surgery, reducing the number of hospital beds still further and passing the burden of care again on to the GP. Nevertheless I will address these issues later in the book and offer helpful strategies for those of you caring for elderly relatives or family members suffering from a psychiatric illness.

The Power Your GP Wields

If we are not feeling physically or mentally "well", we go along to see our GP. We do this as a matter of routine and when we go depends on our own personal definition of "unwell". We rely on the GP's diagnosis to find out what is wrong with us, when *we* feel something is wrong. But the GP has a far more important role than merely diagnosing our complaint. Firstly, such is the power of the GP that we are not ill until the GP says we are and secondly, it is the GP alone who can do something about our illness, be this treatment or advice. If a prescribable medicine is thought appropriate, the GP alone writes the prescription. If a more expert diagnosis or more specialised treatment is required, usually from one of the hospitals, he alone has the power to ask for this. The state will recognise an illness lasting longer than seven days, only if the GP has issued us with a certificate.

But is this a satisfactory way to proceed? Rather, would it not be better, instead of waiting till we are ill to consult the doctor, to consult him when we are well on how to avoid sickness and keep fit? We do not take such a haphazard attitude to our treasured possessions, our cars and houses and household appliances; why should we be so casual with our own bodies? Why not provide for our own continued good health by taking out, as it were, a maintenance contract with our GP? This will, of course, involve a change of view and a change of attitude on our part towards our General Practitioner. It will mean not viewing him an an emergency repair service, but seeing your GP as an expert guide who can develop with you a programme of good health for you and your family at each stage of the life cycle. Of course, this requires the active co-operation of your GP but, fortunately, the modern doctor increasingly sees himself occupying this educational role − where he can put his qualifications to good use in the more egalitarian, less paternalistic way of getting patients to take more responsibility for their health and at the same time have the satisfaction of employing resources more appropriately.

The role of the GP has widened a great deal over recent years. Many activities that used to occur in the hospital regarding the treatment of medical conditions now occur in general practice, for instance, the management of asthma, diabetes, ante-natal care, mental illness and hospital patients discharged early. Many hospital responsibilities, with their associated administrative tasks, have now been reallocated to general practice. Generally, however, the increasingly pivotal role that GPs are being asked to play is not being met with a proportionate increase in resources.

It is as well to bear in mind, therefore, the time constraints that GPs are under these days when choosing a GP that suits you. You need a GP that organises his time well, attends mainly to general practice and is not diverting too many of his energies into outside activities such as family planning, hospital sessions, police work and industrial health consultancies. Enquire when he is available in the practice.

Thus your General Practitioner is of vital importance to you not just in sickness but in health. Only through him do you have access to the National Health Service. He is your advocate as well as being judge of your overall medical condition and counsel for future action. It is essential that you choose him wisely and build a good relationship. In the next two chapters I tell you how to do this.

Living With The NHS From Beginning To End

Stages	Needs
Conception	Good genes/healthy parents/health education
Survive during pregnancy	Good ante-natal care/health education
Survive birth	1st class obstetrics services/post-natal support
Survive infancy & toddlerhood	Good public health & adequate monitoring/excellent GP care
Survive childhood	Avoid accidents & infectious diseases
Reach adulthood	Avoid accidents/survive rare diseases/avoid surgery
Early mid-life 35—45	Live healthily & avoid risks/early cancers/early heart attack/ovarian & cervical cancer
Middle mid-life 45—55	Survive coronaries, cancers & early degenerative disease
Late mid-life 55—65	
Retire & enjoy life 65—? The Third Age	Keep fit/avoid heart attacks/strokes/cancers/degenerative arthritis
Late life	Risk of senile dementia/multi-systems failure
A good death	Pain-free/cared for

2.

The Good GP Guide

In the last chapter I said most people have a more caring attitude towards their house or car or household electrical appliances when it comes to keeping them maintained and in working order than they do towards their own infinitely more precious bodies. On the whole we tend to treat our GP as an emergency service, only consulting him when we do not feel well, or when we feel in pain or when our bodies are not functioning as they should. We wait till something goes wrong before we seek medical help.

Why are we so inconsistent? One of the reasons could be that up till now the National Heath Service has been an illness service, organised to respond only when there is the personal crisis of ill health. It made little or no enquiry as to how that crisis arose and almost no distinction was made between types of illness treated. People felt they could eat and drink what they wanted, burn the candle at both ends and fail to take proper exercise, and then rely on the medical profession to rescue them when their health broke down. A sense of responsibility for our own health was not encouraged by this system.

*Practical Points
Health maintenance. Regular exercise. Healthy diet. No smoking. Limited alcohol. Sense of personal responsibility.

Are You Frightened Of Doctors?
Another reason for failing to consult the doctor to get a proper health estimate on ourselves could be the misplaced sense of respect that doctors engender in all of us, so that we see them only when we think it absolutely necessary. We do not behave in this way towards electricians, builders, plumbers, car mechanics or computer engineers, so why should we be in awe of doctors, who, although

handling more complex subject matter, are, nonetheless, only dealing with the practicalities of making our bodies function properly? If you feel unduly intimidated by doctors, it is essential that you begin to see them as you do any other kind of professional who you consult for his expertise. To profit from the new reforms and the changed health service, we need to consult our GPs on a less awe-struck, more businesslike and practical basis.

It is no accident if you feel this way. Perhaps more than any other profession the medical fraternity has traditionally cultivated an aura of superior detachment. Fortunately, things are changing in this respect. In spite of their strange and complex language, white coats and illegible handwriting, it is being acknowledged more and more, not least by doctors themselves, that they are providing a service and need to become more accessible and accountable to the users of that service and not hide behind any special mystique. And, furthermore, they are there not just to diagnose and treat illness but to educate us in how we should treat our own bodies in maintaining ourselves in good health. The new reforms are also promoting this revised attitude. The Government has set Health-of-the-Nation Targets.

This knowledge should embolden you, when it comes to choosing a doctor for yourself and your family, to do more than just ask friends and neighbours or enquire at the local library. With the new spirit of openness we can be more systematic and purposeful than that and carry out a thoroughgoing appraisal of GPs in our neighbourhood and the services they offer.

Practical Points
Select your GP with care.

Your Plan For Choosing The Right GP

There is a popular notion that GPs are last in the doctors' pecking order, far behind, for example, a neuro (brain) surgeon or heart specialist in prestige and importance. If this ever was the case it certainly no longer is in the 1990s. The GP is now centre stage. The GP determines the kind of treatment you receive. Hospitals and their staff depend for their very existence on the cases the GP *chooses* to send them. They now compete for his custom. Because GPs wield this power and patronage with regard to the health service, it is very important for you to choose a GP who can wield it on your behalf to maximum effect.

My plan for choosing a GP can be rolled into one question, "What resources can this doctor employ on my behalf?" In terms of knowledge, time, money, facilities, ancillary staff and services there are differences between GPs which could be crucial for you in the long run and which mean you should take some time and trouble in choosing the person who is to manage the most precious thing in your life, your health.

Here is my four-point plan for choosing the right GP.

Four Practical Sections

1. Study the practice leaflet

Every practice now has to publish a leaflet which lists the names of the doctors, their sex, their qualifications, the year they qualified and the services offered. The basic qualifications which your doctor will have will be either MB ChB/BS (Bachelor of Medicine and Bachelor of Surgery) and sometimes LRCP (Licenciate of the Royal College of Physicians) and MRCS (Member of the Royal College of Surgeons). He could also have further qualifications from these two Colleges. He may be a member of the Royal College of Psychiatrists (MRCPsych). A Diploma of the Royal College of Obstetricians and Gynaecologists (DRCOG) means he has specialist knowledge of women's diseases, pregnancy and childbirth, whereas a Diploma in Child Health (DCH) means he is qualified to monitor the stages of child development just as a Diploma of the Faculty of Family Planning (DFFP) shows he has special skills in contraception and sexual health. It is important that you find out if your prospective GP has completed vocational training in General Practice. Many excellent older GPs will not have done so as formal training schemes are a recent introduction but, if he is a Member of the Royal College of General Practitioners (MRCGP), then it is a sure demonstration of his commitment to general practice, though not all formally trained GPs have taken the Royal College exams.

Collecting a few practice leaflets will give you, at a glance, a ready comparison of the different practices under consideration. Here are some questions to bear in mind when reviewing these leaflets. First of all, discover if the practice is fundholding or part of a commissioning group, or is single-handed. Next, look at the consulting hours. Do they fit in with the hours you will need to be seen? Is there a surgery on Saturday morning and do they have afternoon surgeries? What are the on call arrangements? Do they rely on a deputising service for out of hours visits or do they share these with other local practices, or do they handle their own calls? The best GPs provide their own cover. Using deputising doctors is understandable but the least satisfactory arrangement.

What special facilities does each practice have? You should be able to find listed a selection of the following clinics: Ante-natal, Wellwoman, Well-man, Geriatric, Child Development and Psychiatric. Are there outreach clinics run by visiting consultants?

What attached staff are there? You should expect to find some of the following personnel mentioned: midwives, health visitors, practice nurses, community psychiatric nurses (CPNs) and social workers.

Overall, as far as you can ascertain, does the practice have resources for your known and likely needs? If you have a chronic problem register with a practice with an interest in that problem. For instance, if you have a psychiatric condition, look for a GP that has qualifications in that field. If you want to be treated by a woman doctor, look for a practice with *two* women doctors so that one will always be available when the other is on leave.

2. Visit the practice

Before committing yourself to a practice go and spend some time observing it in operation and getting a feel for what it is like.

Note the design and material condition of the buildings. Is there enough car parking space; are there facilities for the disabled, a pleasant waiting area and enough consulting rooms to house all the services that the practice is offering? Is the reception area pleasant, clean and tidy? Are there practice information leaflets and posters on display?

Sit in the waiting room and observe how the patients are treated by the receptionists when they present themselves. Are they treated like patients, like customers, or like friends? Listen to the patients. Are they happy or do they moan about the waiting times? Assess how long each consultation takes. Do you feel that confidentiality is preserved? Are the patient notes kept locked-up or kept on open shelving? In other words, are your notes available only to those who should see them? Can you overhear discussions about individual patients taking place in the reception area, either between the receptionists themselves or between a patient and the receptionist? How public are incoming and outgoing phone calls? This is particularly important in small communities.

How are the patients called in to see the doctor? Are they given a number so that they can follow each other in? Does the receptionist call out their name when the doctor signals? Or do the patients sort the order out among themselves when the doctor buzzes? Does the doctor summon each patient over a loudspeaker? Or, ideally, does the doctor come out of the consulting room and personally greet each patient?

How crowded is the waiting room? Do you feel the doctors could be working under so much pressure that they will not have the time to listen to you or deal with your need adequately?

If it is a country practice, does it have its own dispensary?

3. Interview the practice manager

Most practices nowadays have a manager responsible for its organisation and day-to-day running. If it is a fundholding practice it may also employ a fund manager as well. The Government is keen that practices are run on business lines and that each practice has a budget to handle. The budget is subdivided into a drugs budget, a hospital budget and a services budget. At the time of writing, the practice has to have 7,000 patients or more to qualify for fundholding status.

The practice manager is a very important figure in this arrangement because the level and quality of the services the practice can provide depends on his ability to manage the budget efficiently. It is worth spending some time with the practice manager to find out whether the practice is fundholding or not. I recommend you go for a fundholding practice mainly because of the preference patients from these practices receive from hospitals they are contracted to. If you feel happiest with a single-handed practice, many single-handed GPs have banded together to take advantage of the government funding arrangements in so-called commissioning groups.

From the practice manager you will be able to discover what kind of deals have been struck with the local hospitals, what clinics and services are being run from the practice and what sort of appointments system is in place. For example, how long do you have to wait for an appointment, what kinds of patients get priority, are children seen straightaway? Ask about out-of-hours arrangements and home visits.

Practice managers come in all shapes and sizes but at the moment tend to be women who have been promoted from within the ranks of the receptionists, having studied for a diploma in practice management from the local college. However, managers from industry are more and more being recruited. They have the advantage of being conversant with professional personnel, accounting and administrative systems but are disadvantaged in not having a general practice background. General practice is about people; practice staff need to remember this. Many of their patients are scared, unwell and in pain.

4. Interview the GP (who may be male or female)

If you have found a practice you like the look of, why not ask for an appointment with the GP, just to see what he is like and to find out if you have a working relationship? This might seem a novel, even daring idea, but it is all part of the thoroughness that the new system demands and no different from the investigative thoroughness we should employ when deciding to purchase other products or services. Besides, many GPs now like to interview prospective patients to assess their suitability. What you must avoid is being assigned to the list of a doctor you do not know and have never met. It is probably best to arrange the interview through the practice manager.

When you have your interview with the GP, note how it is conducted. Does the doctor give you eye contact? Does he welcome your questions and seem genuinely interested in you? Does he want to give you time? Or does he want to get the interview over with as quickly as possible and get you to fill in the registration forms?

Go with a prepared list of questions. Your questions, of course, will depend on your own individual needs. For instance, if you are a mother with young children, you will probably want to question him on children's development checks and the practice's attitude to children generally, out-of-hours visiting, waiting times and length of appointments, contraceptive services and health visiting. If you have a long term disease, you will need to ask the doctor if he has an interest in that disease or, if not, whether anyone else in the practice has.

You will want to know what his method of referral to the local hospital is, how he gets on with local hospitals and which ones he uses. Confirm whether this is a fundholding or a non-fundholding practice. Make mental notes. Is the GP friendly? Does he convey a sense of trust and confidence? Do you feel he is assertive and adept enough, if needs be, to get you the right hospital consultation at the right time and to get you your share of the resources available?

Do you like him? Look around the room. Look at his certificates. Where and when did he qualify? Where did he register? What are his special interests? Is the room tidy and physically welcoming? Would you feel comfortable and secure getting undressed and being examined in this space? Are there curtains, and hooks to hang your clothes on? Find out what his arrangements are for when he goes on holiday. You might want to find out if the practice has the services of a female doctor. Do you feel that the equipment and facilities reflect a smart, pleasant and capable practice? Remember the doctor spends his working life in this surgery and that the facilities he provides reflect his attitude to patient care and his business management skills.

Taking care to choose a GP and a practice where you will be happy and at ease is the first step in that most vital process, the one which is the foundation of this book: building a good relationship with your chosen GP. What you want is a relationship where you can be open and honest about yourself and your lifestyle and in which you can receive the best help and advice towards functioning independently and well, over the course of your life.

Do not be afraid of actively choosing a GP. Sensible GPs with a modern approach will not feel threatened by a patient assessing them, indeed they will see it as an extension of the practice leaflet-information principle. It is vitally important that you and your GP are happy with each other.

As General Practice becomes recognised for its skills and its importance is reinforced, the Government will face pressure to improve the standards of General Practice, with more and better trained GPs and longer consultation times. The age of the empowered patient may well have arrived, but the inevitable consequence of this is the empowerment of the General Practitioner as well.

The next chapter will look at what happens when you consult your GP and some ways you can start to build your relationship in a responsible, adult way. And it will consider the procedures you should adopt and how doctors communicate with each other about patients when and if you need to be referred to a specialist.

3.

Your GP And Your Health

Is your current GP giving you the treatment you deserve? Is your doctor easy to see? Does he give you enough consultation time? Is his practice well-equipped? Can he accommodate your personal needs?

Maybe you think that your GP is the same as all other GPs and that there is little variation between them. If you do, then you could not be more wrong. There is an enormous variation of standards in terms of service and skills between GPs and it is essential you realise that some GPs are much better than others in skills, facilities and services. The standards of general practice have improved over recent years through the introduction of the vocational training regulations and monitoring by the Family Health Service Authorities (FHSA). But there are still gold standard practices, and other practices which only just scrape in above minimum standards and are a source of concern to their FHSA. Don't expect your GP to be good at everything. Choose the one who is good for you, expert in your problems.

The Differences Between GPs

But surely all doctors belong to the same National Health Service and are subject to the same rules? How can GPs and their practices differ?

Well, for a start, doctors are not employees; they are independently contracted to the FHSA to provide certain medical services to the public (as they have been since the inception of the NHS in 1948). They receive a practice allowance and are also paid a capitation fee for each patient on their list. On top of these they receive fees for the other extra services they provide. From this income they pay themselves, pay their staff and maintain and equip their surgeries. Doctors, therefore, have a certain amount of discretion as to how this income is spent and control how much goes into their own pocket and how much into the practice.

In this way, we see a difference starting to grow between GPs. If you further divide GPs into those who are in single practice and those in group practice, then we can say that on the whole those patients who belong to a group practice will have better facilities than those in a single-handed practice, as both types of practice will face similar overheads but the group practice will have a larger net income from which to fund patient facilities.

At the moment an even wider gap has opened up between GPs: the Government has, in addition, allowed certain GPs to become fund-holders. Those practices with more than 7,000 patients can apply to handle their own budgets for the provision of care for the patients. By shopping around, doing some hard-nosed bargaining and getting value for money, these practices can make their money go even further. Their increased bargaining power also allows them to get priority treatment for their patients from hospitals and other agencies.

Although the new reforms generally favour patients belonging to fundholding group practices it should be borne in mind that there are exceptions. There are some "group" practices where the doctors have banded together only to take advantage of the financial arrangements of the new reforms. But they work badly together without a cohesive, uniform practice policy where the patient comes first. At the same time there are plenty of knowledgeable single-handed GPs who keep abreast of all the latest developments and are particularly good in important areas of primary care, such as child care, gynaecology and asthma. Also, there are GPs who practise from separate premises but are part of a commissioning group of single-handed GPs who operate like a fundholding practice.

Commissioning groups in some areas have been very successful. By having the greater buying power of the large group they have outmanoeuvred the small fundholders. At the same time some District Health Authorities with inspired and capable managers have negotiated exceptional packages as group purchasers for their non-fundholding GPs.

Time For You

There are other things your doctor does or does not do that can make a difference in the quality of treatment you receive. When we summon the resolve to see a doctor, we desire above all else that enough time is allowed for a proper discussion and a considered diagnosis. Anything less and we feel we are not being taken seriously. Many feel that their GP does not have enough time for them.

Practical point
Book more time for a lengthy consultation.

To achieve this the practice needs to have a good appointments system. Some practices do not have any system at all. They operate on a first come, first served basis. The main difficulty here is that if you are worried about something but uncertain whether your problem is sufficiently serious to merit seeing a doctor, you will be discouraged by this system from going to the trouble of waiting your turn. If, on the other hand, you are sufficiently worried to join the queue, you will feel constrained, when you finally see the doctor, about taking up his time if there are still a lot of people waiting to be seen.

It is far better that a practice has an appointments system, but one that is flexible so that if you need to be seen quickly, you can be. A good appointments system will give priority to those who need an early consultation and run a protocol for age groups, so that, for instance, children get priority. The less urgent patients, follow-ups, for example, will be given a place further down the list. A well-organised practice does not book up the first forty five minutes until the day before. A well-organised practice will also have a couple of spare slots for really urgent cases and very small children.

Another area where standards vary, and which gives a good clue to how well-organised and patient-oriented your doctor is, lies in the care of patient notes. Are yours contained in an A4 folder in a tabulated and ordered manner or, equally as good, stored on computer in such a way that your doctor can easily bring himself up to date about you before the interview? Or is he rummaging through a cardboard pouch or peering at the monitor, during your interview, desperately trying to get you into focus? There is, as yet, no paper-free practice; GPs keep written *and* computerised records. They must all be completely secure and confidential.

However, equally important is the time allowed to patients, so that everything that needs to take place in a thorough consultation does so. The minimum time allowed per consultation should be ten minutes. Anything less and you should be looking for a new GP or encouraging him to change his practices. This is a counsel of perfection but, in my opinion, should be a quality standard for general practice. A quality consultation leads to quality care.

In order to put the consultation in perspective, ask yourself this question, "What serious issue could I discuss with my bank manager, solicitor or spouse in less than ten minutes?" Health is a vitally serious issue and a good GP will have a set of procedures for arriving at a sound diagnosis that cannot be got through in less than ten minutes. If you come away from seeing your GP and there are still queries in your mind or if you feel your opinion and worries have not been aired properly, then your GP has doubtlessly skimped some of the necessary steps in arriving at his diagnosis. GPs' lives are busier following the new reforms and most would like to devote more time to the individual interview but time is a resource subject to rationing along with everything else.

The Anatomy Of A Good Consultation

Naturally, an experienced GP will often have a shrewd idea of what ails you very early in the consultation. It is often said by doctors that the most important part of a consultation is the six feet between the door and the chair! But medicine and healing is an interactive, highly personal process in which your own peace-of-mind plays a large part. Any good diagnostic consultation should have the following key elements.

An invitation to describe your symptoms – the presenting complaint, and then a history of your complaint, when it started and how long and with what frequency it has been occurring. Then a pertinent review of your previous medical history, followed by a physical examination relevant to your symptoms, such as heart rate, blood pressure and temperature. At this point your doctor should be able to make a diagnosis and to prescribe treatment. On the other hand, he may decide that you are suffering from a benign self-limiting disease and that no treatment is necessary. That is to say, whatever you have will clear up of its own accord or, knowing he cannot alter the course of your disease, he may decide to prescribe simple medication for the relief of your symptoms. In other words he is limiting the effects of the disease but not curing the disease process itself, as in the case of many viral infections such as 'flu.

If your doctor decides on treatment then he should explain the purpose of the treatment – what he is prescribing and why. He should tell you what the expected outcome of the treatment is and what to do if the treatment does not appear to be working. But remember, many diseases are self-limiting, that is they get better by themselves, and all you really need is reassurance. In some cases he might not be able to treat but knows where to get the help you need, be it the service of a health visitor, a counsellor, a physiotherapist or a social worker. Ideally some of these will be attached to the practice.

When you leave the surgery you need to know what is wrong, what to take and what to do next. However, after going through these preliminary steps, your GP may decide that he is unable to make an accurate diagnosis on the evidence so far and that you will need further tests — tests that can take place then and there with you waiting a few days for the results. Or he may decide to refer you to a consultant at the hospital before a final diagnosis can be arrived at. Again, your doctor should keep you fully informed as to what he is doing and why. He should tell you when and how to stop the treatment and how soon you should inform him if it is not working.

*Practical point
Clearly understand the disease, the treatment and the follow-up.

It is essential that you have realistic expectations of your GP before making a judgement on his performance. He might decide that advice and reassurance is the best treatment for you, for instance in the case of a benign self-limiting disease. But he should always keep you in the picture. As a non-expert you have no idea how consequential your symptoms might be. Your GP may decide that no treatment is necessary, but a good GP will inform and educate you and by this means give you what, in a way, is treatment in itself — peace-of-mind.

The doctor has to diagnose what is wrong with you and needs to set aside enough time for finding out. You, for your part, must be open and honest with him. He can read your symptoms but he cannot read your mind. This is especially true of anything of a psychiatric or sexual nature. If you cannot talk to your doctor openly about your problems, change your doctor. But trust is a two way process and you need to go half way to meet him.

It may be that a patient is suffering multiple problems, for example stomach pains, piles, rectal bleeding and loss of weight, where a normal ten minute appointment would not be sufficient. It would be a good idea and perfectly in order to request a longer appointment at a mutually convenient time to have these more thoroughly investigated.

GPs have different consulting styles, ranging from autocratic to democratic, from firmly instructing the patient to involving the patient in the decisions. It is up to you which style you prefer. The main thing is that you interact easily with your GP and that you feel he is taking you seriously.

The Advantage Of The Fundholder

When it comes to getting you the best treatment, the fundholding GP has more clout than his non-fundholding colleague, particularly at the end of the financial year! For some common procedures the GP will know from past experience how many patients he is likely to refer. He can then renegotiate a block contract with the hospital that gives him the best price. Which means that patients of his requiring routine surgery, such as hip replacement or removal of gallstones, can be seen by a consultant and operated on without undue delay. It might mean travelling outside your area but that is a small price to pay for avoiding queues and a likely succession of cancelled operations.

The fundholding GP can offer a whole range of services that can make a difference to your treatment and personal convenience. Has your doctor the ability and experience to do minor surgery? Does he offer the services of a physiotherapist? Does he have consultants visiting the surgery? Does he employ his own health visitor or, in the case of the elderly, does he arrange domiciliary consultations with the local hospital? Does he run specialised clinics for asthma, diabetes, child health, well-man/woman? Does he have a phone-in service where you can discuss symptoms before deciding whether to make an appointment or not? Does the practice provide counsellors? All this helps to prevent spending valuable hours hanging around an outpatient clinic or doctor's waiting room. It is more likely that the fundholding GP will offer these services than the non-fundholder.

Many GPs have special interests in particular aspects of medicine and will run clinics at the surgery reflecting their interest. Other GPs will do work for certain departments at the local hospital as well. This is a good thing, if done in moderation, since, not only will they be skilled in their own speciality but, having the stimulus of the hospital environment, they will be knowledgeable about other specialised areas of medicine as well. It is a good idea to find out what areas of medicine the GPs in your practice are interested in and how that interest is manifested. However be wary of GPs who work at night possibly for a deputising service or for the police. It is difficult to see how a modern GP can do much of this and at the same time offer a proper service to his patients.

It is worth noting that a fundholding GP does not profit by not sending you to hospital. If he doesn't spend the sum that has been allocated to him, the amount for the following year will be cut accordingly. Nor does he profit financially by sending you to certain consultants; fee splitting was outlawed many years ago.

Ethically fundholders should in no way benefit from any savings they might make. Funds should not be directed away from patient-care, the purpose for which they are intended. Fundholding is, at the moment, still in its relatively early stages. The administrative costs are high and subsidised by the taxpayer in terms of administrative support. Yet some GPs are already leaving fundholding schemes, dissatisfied with the administrative load that is still imposed. Inevitably some fundholders will run out of budget or mismanage their budget with serious consequences for their patients. As yet, GPs are doctors with limited business skills. Generally, however, fundholders' patients will probably benefit compared with non-fundholders'. Nevertheless, some skillfully managed District Health Authorities do better at purchasing services from Trust hospitals for their non-fundholding GPs than do some inefficient, individual fundholders.

However, it is worth pointing out that the mechanism now exists, with the rising costs of treatment and increasing demand on the NHS, for Governments now and in the future to blame the inefficiency and mismanagement of fundholders if treatment is delayed or denied, when in fact the money may not have been made available in the first place and such blame is out of order.

Different Types Of Referral

There is an aspect of the new system which demands extra vigilance from patients and their relatives, and that is where a condition is diagnosed which demands treatment from a consultant specialising in that condition. Most conditions can be dealt with by the consultants at your district general hospital; nevertheless, there are some conditions that need specialised referral outside your area. Sometimes these experts will be found in departments outside the region where you live when there are no inter-regional arrangements for funding such patients. Or the expert may be working at a centre of excellence in the region but your doctor has no arrangement with such a centre. For instance, there are certain forms of cancer which need to be treated by someone specialising solely in these disease states. Bowel cancer and breast cancer require the informed judgment of someone who has narrowed his expertise to these particular branches of medical knowledge.

The removal of an appendix or the repair of a hernia are straightforward procedures available at any local district general hospital. However, if you are referred for something more complex, like a heart condition, it is as well to ask who you are being referred to, does he have a special interest in your condition? If an operation is likely, say a coronary artery bypass graft, how many does he perform in a year, what is his mortality rate?

The good GP knows the right place to go for the right treatment. He will be prepared to fight for the funds to get you the appropriate treatment at the appropriate centre. It should not be up to the patient to have to go over the GP's head to an MP or the Ombudsman at a worrying and distressing time to secure this for themselves.

The best treament, like anything of excellence, is expensive. It is available but not readily available. Because the Government has decided to introduce the market mechanism into the health service every disease is now priced. Theoretically the best treatment is available to all. However, if you are living in the wrong part of the country, away from a centre of excellence, your chances of receiving the right specialist help are diminished. If you do not belong to a fundholding practice they tend to be lessened still further. And, if your GP has not got the drive and assertiveness to win you the treatment you need and deserve but is content just to put you in a queue at the local hospital to be treated by a general surgeon or a general physician, they are non-existent.

As yet the public is not schooled in weighing up the cost factors involved in medical treatment. Our cultural expectations are that whatever we need in the form of treatment is readily available and, for certain routine procedures, it is. But when we come to expensive treatment market forces ration the supply. As we saw in Chapter 1, there is no stage of our life when we might not have need of specialist treatment. It is now vital that you anticipate getting access to them by signing on with the right GP, one who has the acumen to interfere with market forces.

Home Visits
Part of our false expectation as to what is available in terms of medical help stems from a cultural notion, unique to the British, that medical help is available twenty four hours a day, that we can summon a doctor to our home any time we wish, outside surgery hours. If we are prepared to demand the best treatment from our GP when there is something seriously wrong with us, we must exercise thought and restraint before using the precious resource of after hours visiting. From the taxpayers' point of view, if you think how expensive it is to call out a plumber or an electrician these days, how

much more expensive is it to call out a doctor? So, from the point of view of using your GP as a personal resource, it is wise to avoid putting your doctor under any unnecessary pressure.

The average GP will spend three hours in the morning and two hours in the evening seeing patients in surgery. The rest of his day will be spent visiting patients who are confined to their homes and in doing an ever increasing amount of paperwork. Some afternoons will be devoted to special clinics. Most GPs work a minimum of ten hours a day. Giving some thought as to how and when you call out your GP is essential if you are to build a mature relationship, where you are seen as a responsible and serious individual which, in turn, commends you as a person and strengthens your case when you are seeking the help of the GP to work the system on your behalf should you, or a member of your family, happen to become seriously ill.

Here are some points to bear in mind when deciding whether to call out your doctor.

Question: Is the condition immediately life threatening, such as loss of consciousness, fitting, difficulty in breathing, severe injury such as falls, burns or serious bleeding? If so, then dial 999, clearly give the information requested and ask for a paramedic ambulance. Paramedic ambulances have crews specially skilled in managing acute emergencies.

Question: Do you have chest pains? If in doubt, call your GP for advice but in general, if you suspect a heart attack, it is best to call a paramedic ambulance which will be equipped to start treatment straightaway. If it is a heart attack, the quicker treatment is started the more chance there is of preserving heart function and making a good recovery afterwards. Many lives could be saved by getting early expert help.

*Practical point
We all have a personal responsibility to learn basic resuscitation skills. Cardiopulmonary resuscitation (CPR), in my opinion, should be taught to all eleven year olds, and again to all school leavers and should be compulsory before the issue of a driver's licence and not just left to Boy Scouts, Girl Guides, St John's Ambulance and "the professionals".

For anything else where doubts are raised in your mind, especially concerning the very young and the very old, or someone with a chronic disease that has suddenly worsened, contact your GP and be prepared to answer questions and take advice over the phone. The GP, on hearing the symptoms, may advise you to dial 999.

I hope it goes without saying that conditions where simple remedies are available or those that can wait without serious deterioration for surgery opening time, such as coughs, colds, sore throats, runny noses, urinary tract infections or long standing chronic problems, are not sufficiently serious for a home visit. By having the doctor visit your home to attend to minor symptoms or renew a prescription, you could be delaying him from attending someone in dire need of his services.

When you phone your GP after hours, state the facts clearly and give reasons for your worries about a particular problem which you feel might be urgent. If your GP doesn't feel it is urgent, be prepared to receive advice and an early appointment instead of a home visit; it will go a long way towards increasing mutual respect between the two of you. The Government will shortly be introducing out-of-hours centres which you will be expected to attend if you ring your doctor when the surgery is closed. You will be entitled to a home visit but only if you can convince the doctor of its necessity.

*Practical point
Your GP is available 24 hours a day, 365 days a year, either personally or by delegation. Remember, out-of-hours this service is for emergencies only.

Nor will it cement the relationship with your GP if you regard the Accident and Emergency Department at your local hospital as a convenient place to get attention for general medical problems, or to get a second opinion, or as a way to queue jump. There is a false notion abroad that A&E is a supplement or even an alternative to general practice. Like out-of-hours calls to GPs, Accident and Emergency is only there to deal with matters of an urgent and serious nature. We had better get used to the fact that in today's health service there are no luxury items.

We all pay for the health service so it is in all our interests to make use of our GP outside his normal working hours only when it is absolutely necessary. Of course, to see a doctor privately is always an option open to us. Currently you can expect to pay £15−£20 for a fifteen minute in-surgery consultation and £60 per hour for a home visit, including travelling time.

Your GP And The Treatment Of Mental Illness

What do you do if you think you are, or a member of your family is, mentally ill and you think your GP is not doing enough? Go and discuss it with him in an open and honest fashion and tell him what the problem is. Do not be afraid to admit that you are ill and be prepared to accept help. Recognition of your problem is part of treatment. You will need to book in advance and make it clear that you have a long, time-consuming problem. It is a good idea to take a close friend with you, someone who knows you well and can say how your problem is affecting the people in your domestic, social and work circle. Make sure you have a clear account of what the doctor's diagnosis is and what all the treatment options are. Do not be pushed into having medication without knowing what other alternatives there might be. Ask for a referral to a psychiatrist or psychologist if the management of mental illness is not a speciality of your GP.

GPs do have some training in the management of mental illness and mental health problems but most are not expert and do not have time to treat these patients properly. There are specialists expert in particular aspects of mental illness, just as there are specialists in narrow areas of general medicine or surgery. You should consider asking for a referral to a specialist in the field of your particular illness. You may be faced with a long wait as this area of referral is under-resourced. Be prepared to ask for the support of a community psychiatric nurse (CPN) or a social worker or health visitor. Some mental illnesses can be assuaged by alleviating the social pressures that have triggered them, such as pressures of a financial or business nature. Marital pressures could perhaps be handled by Relate (formerly the Marriage Guidance Council).

Practical point

If you have suicidal thoughts or intent, or one of your relatives does, then urgent discussion with your GP is vital and may save a life. The Samaritans (in your local phone book) could be an essential contact too.

The Difficult Elderly Relative

Another problem which frequently confronts families is the difficult elderly relative. Here again, your GP is working in the context of chronic underfunding and lack of resources. He will do his best to help you solve your problems but his chances of success increase markedly the more you can help. Here the right approach is essential. You and your GP have to work together to solve, alleviate or control the problem. The first thing you have to do is define the problem then go along and discuss it with him so that together you can develop a plan of action. All GPs should now be screening the elderly, so the first thing to do is to ensure that all treatable causes of any disease which might be destroying the personality of your elderly or infirm relative are excluded. Tactfully suggest to your GP that your relative's health needs are reviewed, including medication, and that drug interaction problems are also excluded. If the resources of the GP fail to solve the problem ask for referral to a Geriatrician or a Psychiatrist or a Psychogeriatrician. It is in these cases where the specialist can see the patient in their own home environment that a domiciliary visit often proves to be the best solution. The recommendation for re-housing or admission, following a domiciliary visit, frequently breaks the log-jam of accumulated problems.

In the longer term, try to arrange with the GP for your relative to have a regular review of their medical needs. Amid the urgent clamour of modern life we often fail to make time for the important things and become forgetful of those for whom we bear some responsibility. Many of the sad, neglected elderly could lead happier lives if their relatives and those around them in the community showed them more care and kindness and visited on a regular basis. In Britain today, the Asian community provides an example of how the elderly can be appreciated and cared for as part of the extended family.

Practical point
Try to plan in advance. Have strategies and contingency plans prepared. Avoid crisis management.

Be Realistic
You will make the best use of your GP if your expectations of what he can and cannot do are realistic. We can be made to feel trapped and miserable by any number of circumstances in our life. Maybe one's love life is a disaster or the boss is a bully or we have fallen out with family members. Stresses such as these can have physical effects — headaches, fatigue and stomach upset. The doctor can treat

all these, he can also prescribe tranquillisers and antidepressants to lift our mood but he would only be treating *symptoms* when the underlying causes may be social and non-medical. The GP and his practice team will always give advice but they have a limited capacity to change the social circumstances of their patients' lives. When deciding to see our GP we have to make up our minds if we are unwell due to bodily dysfunction or disease or whether it is due instead to understandable human misery, an emotional ache which no medicine or surgical procedure can ever fix.

We are now entering the era of patient choice. The benign paternalism of the past is rapidly fading. We now have dual responsibility with our GP for our own treatment, developed through negotiation and dialogue. To benefit from the new health reforms we need to know if we are getting the best treatment possible. This may mean scrutinising a doctor's qualifications, how he runs his practice, what resources he can deploy on our behalf, and his ability to refer us and get the appropriate treatment. We need someone we can talk to and who is able to keep us in the picture. And yet, even if he fulfils all these criteria, we need someone who will get us a second opinion when we request it and who has a complaints procedure in place if we are unhappy.

General Practice is vitally important and needs to be properly supported, funded and staffed. If the Government truly believes in competition, it should allow patients greater scope in choosing their GP.

The way in which General Practice is developing needs input from the consumer/patient. Patients recognise the need for longer consultation times and so do most GPs. It is pressure of work and demands made on the service which result in the GP having to see patients in unacceptably short consultation times. General Practice is improving, but unless the number of trained GPs increases, a crisis may well occur as older GPs approach retirement. The public need not be embarrassed about attempting to join in the debate about the deployment of healthcare resources, by outlining what they would like in a GP and his practice. Indeed, as the GPs' workload increases with more patients consulting and more paperwork, most GPs would welcome our support by making our preferences known about General Practice, how it should develop and how its services could be better delivered.

Going Private

Patients can also opt to be treated privately by a GP or Consultant. There are private (non-NHS) GPs who exclusively treat private patients and it is possible to be treated as a private patient by an NHS GP. If you are a private patient of a GP, you cannot have an NHS prescription; you must pay for all treatment on the private network. It is not possible to mix NHS and private treatment. However, you can be referred by your NHS GP privately to a hospital consultant. If the consultant decides you need an operation, you can opt to be treated in private hospital facilities at your own or your insurance company's expense. What is clearly unethical is for you to be seen as a private outpatient by a consultant and then for you to gain an advantage by being put onto the NHS waiting or operating list in a higher position than if you had been seen by the consultant on the NHS on the same day at the same time. What is clearly unfair is for the patient to jump an NHS waiting list by being seen as a private outpatient.

It is, however, perfectly fair and reasonable for you to choose to be a private patient and opt to spend your hard-earned cash to get a specific problem treated privately because there is a long NHS waiting list. For example, a hernia operation done privately could make good commercial sense to a self-employed lorry driver who might otherwise have to wait up to a year. If you have varicose veins or need a similar operation no longer available in your local Trust, you may have no option but to have it done privately.

Private healthcare is an option that we should all consider for routine hospital treatment. (But be aware that private care does not come cheap.) You can pay yourself or obtain cover under one of the many private and competitive insurance schemes. Some people prefer to do this as the standard of care in private medicine in terms of consultation times, waiting times, facilities and surroundings are those to which the NHS aspires.

Some NHS patients may be provided with appointments at three minute intervals with consultants. On this basis, a consultant would expect to see up to ten NHS patients in the same time that he allocates to one private patient.

Consultants have a contract with the NHS for a maximum of 38½ hours a week; most give many more hours "free". What a consultant does in his own time is, often literally, his own business.

In the next chapter we will plumb the mysteries of the hospital service and learn how, by asking the right questions and targeting the key people, we will be able to get the best out of it and use it to our advantage.

4.

Referring You Into
Secondary Care

Most of the decisions we make in life are not very important. However, from time to time we are called upon to make a decision that has lifelong consequences, such as choosing a partner, a career or parenthood. I hope my book so far has impressed you with the fact that choosing the right GP is one of those life-changing decisions. It is one the importance of which has in the past unfortunately been disguised by the false mystique surrounding the medical profession and by the assumptions underlying the old health service. To benefit from the new health service we must give more consideration to choosing our doctor.

The best GPs run a health maintenance programme through which they diagnose and treat most problems before they develop into something more serious. Outside one of these programmes, most of us are likely to consult our GP only once a year or so for the rest of our lives. For most of the time the problem will be resolved with that visit. A good GP will have the competence to deal with the symptoms we describe to him then and there but will also have the wisdom to recognise symptoms that are beyond the resources he commands to deal with them. It is at this point, when we need to be referred to a hospital consultant, that we tend to find the consequences of choosing or not choosing the right GP most fully realised.

What I am going to consider in this chapter is the occasion when you consult your GP about a problem which he is unable to resolve directly. He thinks the problem needs further investigation so he refers you to an appropriate hospital specialist.

We saw in Chapter 1 that there are certain common disease states that correspond to particular age groups and which are serious enough to warrant hospital treatment. Although we cannot predict if we will succumb to a particular illness at any age, it is, nonetheless, prudent to anticipate being referred and entering a hospital as a patient before it happens.

It could happen at any time in your life and possibly at a time when you are feeling vulnerable and fearful, when you might not have the presence of mind to ask the right questions or to check if the right thing is being done on your behalf.

Practical point
Being referred to hospital or for tests provokes significant anxiety in all of us. We worry about pain, discomfort and indignity, the possible consequences and ultimately the threat to our mortality. Our first referral for what could be a potentially serious illness brings with it the realisation, possibly for the first time, that we are going to die one day. Overtly or covertly, anxiety is there for everyone who is referred and it is well to remember this, too, when it happens to those who are close to you.

The Internal Market
Before moving on to examine the process of being referred and how to handle it, we need to examine the new background against which all of this will now occur. I have said that the main plank of the new health reforms is the creation of an internal market. Although this is hardly apparent when you visit your GP, apart from a greater array of services if you are part of a fundholding practice, in the hospital sector the internal market reform is having a great impact, and you as a patient need to be aware of the possible benefits and, more importantly, the hidden pitfalls.

The Health Service Act of 1946 decreed that the treatment would be free at the point of use and that no money would change hands. Nearly fifty years later this principle has been overturned and almost all hospitals now exist solely on the money they can attract from fundholding GPs and the bulk contracts placed by Health Authorities. If hospitals fail to win this business then whole departments are liable to close down with the doctors and their staff being made redundant. This has already started to happen. We may yet see the evolution of the "hyper" Hospital, Trusts merging and, eventually, more local hospitals closing.

Like any other enterprise in the economy the very survival of the new Trust hospitals depends upon the business they win with the services they can provide at an acceptable price. Also, like any other business, each hospital has to decide which sector of the market to occupy — low-cost quick turnover items or high cost specialist ones; large volume goods or niche market specialist jobs. However, the internal market diverges from real business practice in this respect: nobody gains financially from these transactions. Any profits that are made are put back into the system.

The new system, therefore, puts hospital managers under severe pressure to opt for the quick high turnover items, the common complaints that afflict the majority of the population: nothing too complicated, nothing too time-consuming. Which means that a further principle of the free market now enters the picture — the principle of 'buyer beware!' You now need to ensure that you are not being treated as a high turnover item when you need more specialised treatment and to remember that although your GP may have a contract with a particular hospital, it does not necessarily follow that it is the best hospital to treat your complaint.

You may also need to be aware that there are not enough specialist doctors for everyone that needs them. Because there are pressures on managers to operate on very thin profit margins they are converting specialist departments in their hospitals into general departments. On the whole, new centres of excellence are not being opened and the old ones are contracting or disappearing altogether. You need your GP to know where these are and to fight to get you a referral.

The Referral Letter

Let us assume your GP wants you to see a hospital consultant. It is now that the trouble you have taken to choose the right GP starts to pay off. First of all he has to make a decision: to which consultant to refer you. If he is a fundholder he will be able to consider consultants beyond your local district hospital. He can even refer you privately. Fundholding GPs have the power and the resources to pay for your treatment in a private hospital if this is the best deal they can get. So if your GP is a fundholder you can find yourself being treated in a private bed on the NHS. Paradoxically, a fellow taxpayer, living a few doors away but registered with a non-fundholding GP, could find himself at the bottom of a long waiting list. If your GP is a non-fundholder he may have difficulty getting around the normal rules for patients funded by local health authorities in order to obtain an ECR, an Extra Contractual Referral.

Having selected the right specialist for what he thinks is your complaint and having discussed it with you, he will write a referral letter. Depending on the type and quality of letter he writes depends when you get seen and the quality of the consultation.

The first item of information that has to be imparted to the consultant is the GP's own presumptive diagnosis. There is no room here for vagueness or selectivity. A clear description of the symptoms is vital. There is wide variation among GPs as to the number of patients they refer. A poor GP will over-refer. He is probably someone who has not kept abreast of the latest developments by going on courses, attending lectures at the post graduate medical centre or at his local medical school, by reading the latest books and current journals or even by conferring with his colleagues. He has not got enough confidence in his own diagnostic ability to initiate treatment so he plays safe by referring the patient on. This means that he acquires a reputation at the local hospital for wasting their time and resources. As a result his referrals are not taken as seriously as those of his more capable colleagues. Your GP should at least get the referral to the correct department of the hospital.

Besides outlining your symptoms, your doctor will need to state what he thinks is the degree of urgency. Again, doctors who overstate this in order to get priority for their parents soon get a "cry wolf" reputation and are subsequently not taken seriously. A good indicator of your GP's standing with a consultant is whether he is able to telephone him, especially on an urgent referral.

Urgency will range from the discovery of, for example, an ectopic pregnancy which demands immediate admittance into the hospital and surgery within the hour, or a breast lump or ovarian cyst which needs to be looked at within forty eight to seventy two hours to know if they are malignant or not, to a fibroid uterus or bladder problem which needs to be examined promptly but can be investigated within a longer time frame.

If your doctor has to be open and clear in his communication with the consultant, it is vitally important that you mention everything about your condition that causes you concern. This is not time for British reticence, understatement or misplaced bravery. If you think in your heart of hearts that your condition is urgent then make a case for yourself. It is up to your GP to 'sell' you to the consultant as a priority case and the more relevant information you can give him to help do this, the better. However, although it is important not to understate how you feel about your condition, it is equally important not to exaggerate.

It is as well to know that there is no correlation between the time it takes a consultant to see you and the time it takes him to get you admitted for treatment should he so decide. You can wait a long time for your outpatient appointment and then you can be admitted very quickly afterwards, or you could be seen very quickly and have to wait a long time for a hospital bed. If, however, after two weeks you have not received your appointment, ring the consultant's secretary to see if a letter has been sent. If it has, find out the reason for the delay in giving you an appointment. If the letter has not been sent ring your GP and ask why not.

Practical point
It is in your interests for you to "progress chase". Progress chasing is a very important activity.

I have said that from now on we need to view our GP as a partner in the management of our health. It probably demands an adjustment on our part to see the GP like any other kind of expert, in this situation merely one who happens to offer us professional advice on repairing and maintaining our health. Now we need to carry this attitude forward and apply it to our dealings with whatever hospital to which we may be referred.

Attending The Hospital
Because hospitals are, on the whole, large, bureaucratic organisations trying to be as efficient as possible with limited resources, they can appear impersonal. Certainly, in the past, they have not had a good record of keeping patients in the picture in terms of their treatment and prognosis, or of allowing family and friends ready access to the patient before or after treatment.

Once you start dealing with hospitals it is very easy to feel intimidated. You are isolated from your own familiar environment, surrounded by professionals and experts who seem to assume rights over you because you have been designated 'sick' and who assume, because they have professional and scientific knowledge to deal with your sickness, that you will not understand what is going on. If you add to this your own fear of the unknown and your feelings of vulnerability, the experience is going to be less than happy.

It is important that you discuss with your GP the kind of consultant to whom you are being referred and whether he is working in a centre having the proper allied facilities; that is to say, if you need to be cross-referred, will he be able to do it easily? For instance, I know a very good maternity unit which achieves a high degree of satisfaction among mothers who have given birth there. It is small and friendly and patients feel cared for. However, if there are complications and specialist care is needed, in the form of a neonatal unit or an emergency caesarean, they have to be rushed up to the main hospital, half an hour's journey away.

When you go to take up your outpatient appointment, try to go with a friend for back-up and certainly go with a list of prepared questions. Treat this as a two-way exchange. You will need to feel satisfied that you will be receiving the right treatment in a manner that is personal, dignified and expert.

When you go for your appointment there are some pointers to look out for. How are you received? Does it compare with the manner of your reception at the GP's surgery? Or at your local florist, hairdresser or vet's practice for that matter? Or perhaps for men, how does it compare to the reception in a new car showroom? Is there a seat for everyone? Do you have to wait longer than half an hour — the amount of time stipulated in the Government's Patient's Charter. Are your privacy and dignity respected? If you are told to undress, are you then left waiting without any clothes for an uncomfortable length of time? Are there screens for you to get undressed behind and are there hooks on which to hang your clothes?

*Practical point
Your privacy and dignity should be respected; ensure they are.

As part of the new customer-oriented ethos of the health service all staff should wear name badges and introduce themselves. Expect the doctor to introduce himself and say who he is. If he does not, ask. Besides knowing the name of the doctor you should be able to find out his grade. If you are seen by a Senior House Officer (SHO) ask to see the consultant. You may, however, be seen by the Senior Registrar. This is acceptable as he works closely with the consultant and will be eligible for a consultant post in the near future. For minor conditions such as a hernia you could be examined by a junior registrar. In the hospitals in my region it is the policy that any new patient will always be seen by a consultant. It is recognised that consultants in the main get the diagnosis right and that problems with inappropriate investigations or stalling tactics which result from inexperience are thus avoided.

*Practical point
Ask to see the consultant.

The Hospital Consultation

It is important to like the consultant with whom you are dealing. By
this I mean he should seem approachable, appear to listen and to be
interested in you and your problem. As with your GP, you need to
ensure that there are no barriers to communication, that you both
understand each other. When the consultation is over you need to
have the answers to all the following questions clearly in your mind.

*Practical point
1.   What is wrong with me?
2.   What needs to be done to me?
3.   What will be the outcome?
4.   What are the risks?
5.   What are the alternatives?
6.   Who is doing it?
7.   Is he an acknowledged expert in his field?
8.   Where will it be done?
9.   When will it be done?
10. How can I help myself?

If the consultant decides you need surgery ask what his operative
infection and complication rates are. If he does not know, request he
posts them to you. Every surgical team now has to keep a record of
this as part of each department's internal audit. Doctors are keen on
audit. It allows them to improve their practice and put pressure on
management for extra resources. In the near future, the Government
is hoping to publish detailed performance figures for consultants.
The quality of these statistics is yet unknown.

If the doctor does not devote himself solely to treating the
condition that is being diagnosed, ask if he has had special training
in that condition or if it is an area of special interest. If he wishes
to operate, find out how many such operations he performs in a year.

Given our past conditioning about doctors it will take guts to ask
the consultant, basically: "Are you any good?" But always remember
this; under the new rules you are the customer and the hospitals are
there to work for you.

If the consultant wants to order tests, make sure you know why he
is doing so, what the comparative risks are and what alternative tests

there are. For instance, he may want you to have an x-ray with a barium enema (a specialist bowel x-ray with liquid being poured into the rectum) where colonoscopy (a flexible telescope being inserted up the back passage into the bowel) would yield better results.

If you are diagnosed as suffering from a long-term medical condition and are put on drugs, ask how long he envisages the treatment will last and what are the possible side-effects, the likely improvements and the natural history of the disease.

Don't be misled by appearances. It is possible to have a hospital which fulfils many of the criteria: welcoming staff, friendly consultants, pleasing surroundings and yet which, at the end of the day, does not have a very good treatment record. It is like going to a restaurant which is the last word in decor and waitress service but which burns the food. Alternatively, you can have hospitals housed in ramshackle premises which are cold and impersonal but staffed by brilliant clinicians with impressive results.

If you are seriously ill, the NHS still provides the best range of clinicians and the best facilities. Not all hospitals have an ITU (Intensive Care Unit) but there are well-equipped ones with 24 hour consultant cover at most of the regional centres. If you are to undergo a serious operation make sure there is one available for you as back-up. In my experience not many private hospitals offer this facility.

The Pros And Cons Of The New System

Not all hospitals are the same and not all GPs are the same. We are now operating part of the health service as an internal market and, I repeat, the message of this book is "buyer beware". Beware that you have a good GP; beware that he belongs to a fundholding practice; beware that, if necessary, he can choose the right consultant for your medical problem; beware that the consultant is right for you, that he keeps you in the picture. It is good that we are being urged to exercise choice and to become aware that there are variable standards within the health service. Greater public awareness of what is good medical practice and what is not is bound to drive up standards.

But is this a fair system? Are not many patients being disadvantaged because they live away from the urban centres or, perhaps, because they belong to the practice of one of the many single-handed GPs offering a personalised service to a manageable list, or, maybe, because they have been diagnosed as untreatable? The answer to these latter questions has to be, I'm afraid, that there are still many problems. You and I have not been consulted about the radical changes made in our health service and in my view we need a national debate, and one that is not party political, in order to resolve the issue of health rationing in the most equitable way. This will also relieve the terrible pressure upon doctors and managers who, at the moment, have to decide who gets treatment and who does not, on economic rather than clinical grounds.

The fact is that at present not all taxpayers are equal in the healthcare market. As a citizen there are mechanisms for getting involved in the running of the health service, through Community Health Councils, your elected representatives in Parliament and locally, and the annual consultative meeting of your local Trust hospital, but it is beyond the scope of this book to describe them here. In the meantime, I can only advise you of the best way of using the only system we have. Despite official denials, there is rationing and you need to get your share of resources.

I have now brought you to the point where you have seen the consultant, recommended by your GP. He will, most probably, have conducted tests. If those tests are positive he may want you admitted into hospital for treatment. In the next chapter I will show you how hospitals work, how to interpret what's happening to you and how best to participate in the treatment you are undergoing. I will show you, too, how to get treated quicker if you are at the end of a very long queue.

5.

Going Into Hospital

Modern hospitals are big and complex organisations. As a patient unfamiliar with the hospital environment it is easy to feel overwhelmed and confused by the many different departments and the many different types of doctor you encounter there. The strange sounding names for the different departments and a spoken language full of medical jargon makes going into hospital seem like travelling to a distant country. This chapter will be a guide and map to this new country so you will have some idea of what is going on and feel less helpless and more in command when you are admitted into hospital.

How Hospital Services Are Organised

The priority you are given as a patient is dictated by your condition. If your condition is diagnosed as being acute then you will be given high priority and early treatment. Apart from the Accident and Emergency Department, which is there to deal directly with acute cases not referred by GPs, each department has a twenty four hour rota with a consultant-led team, known as a firm, "on take" ready to take acute cases which have been diagnosed by the patient's GP. For example, there is a surgical team on stand-by to treat urgent conditions such as perforated ulcer or acute bowel obstruction; a medical team for conditions like heart attack; an orthopaedic team to set broken bones; an obstetrics (baby matters) and gynaecology (women's matters) team and a paediatric team for sick children. Routine, planned admissions for surgery or investigation are known as elective, or, colloquially, as "cold" admissions.

A consultant from each speciality will do an outpatient clinic several times a week and that is where your GP will refer you if he thinks you are not an acute case. The consultant, on behalf of the GP, will decide what treatment or what further investigation is needed. For example, if your GP suspects, from the symptoms you describe, that you have a chronic ulcer and the gastro-enterologist is of the same mind then he will arrange for you to attend the endoscopy clinic so that one of his team can visually examine the inside of your stomach with a special telescope to find out if this is correct.

As well as doing outpatient clinics, many consultants do outreach clinics held in health centres, usually those of fundholding GPs. They also visit patients' homes at the request of a GP, which is known as a domiciliary visit. These visits tend to be almost exclusively to old people or people with a psychiatric illness and they are usually to assess if these patients would be better off in hospital. These are all factors that impinge on the time for which a consultant is contracted to the NHS and they therefore affect the waiting times of patients in the non-acute category. No consultant can predict the volume of acute cases at any one time, so it should be obvious that an abnormal acute load is liable to lengthen the waiting time of the non-acute patient still further. The growing administrative burden on consultants as they are drawn more and more into the running of the new Trust hospitals also limits the consultants' time with the patients.

When making a non-acute referral your GP has to assess the degree of urgency of your condition. He will either label it 'urgent', 'early' or 'routine'. The GP will have a list of waiting times for each consultant. It is regrettable but true that the best consultants usually have the longest waiting lists. Nevertheless, there is also a lack of resources and underfunding in some specialities such as rheumatology which means there is a national shortage of experts in these fields. You have to decide, along with your GP, if it is worth waiting that extra amount of time for the consultant who is an acknowledged expert. Often it can be a real dilemma, a balance of risks and benefits, where there is no clear cut answer.

Where there is non-acute, long term illness, especially psychiatric and psychogeriatric illness, or mental handicap, you will probably find there are not many in-patient beds available.

Hospital Doctors And The Jobs They Do
You are the patient of your GP. He is responsible for your healthcare. You are only 'lent' to others. The GP has twenty-four hour responsibility for your care. His responsibility is to treat you when you are ill or likewise provide someone qualified in his place, a partner, a locum, a deputising doctor or a hospital specialist, if needs be. GPs are self-employed, independent contractors responsible to their local Family Health Service Authority (FHSA)

for providing this service.

Hospital doctors and nurses are civil servants paid for by the taxpayer and are employees of the Trust running their hospital. The Trusts have contracts with the community to provide care in specified areas, part of the purchaser-provider relationship, with the hospital being the provider. Each consultant is part of a directorate within a Trust. He has a contractural obligation to the Trust and an obligation to you, the patient, to provide treatment within specified services. But a doctor's professional code means that his obligation to his patients overrides all other considerations, which may entail freely speaking out on behalf of his patients.

When you go into hospital you will be attended to by a succession of doctors. Many will wear white coats and have stethoscopes round their necks but there are important differences between them of grade and responsibility which are important to know.

The Consultant

The consultant is the leader of a team within a hospital which provides diagnosis and treatment for you, the patient. He is fully trained, fully accredited and responsible for your total care during your stay in the hospital. The name of your consultant will be on your bed's headboard and on any paperwork that might be given to you. If you do not know the name of your consultant, you must ask. You are entitled to be seen and treated by your consultant but clearly and quite rightly, in his executive role, he will delegate various tasks to competent members of his team.

When you are in hospital, ask what sort of consultant he is. Most consultants have a special interest; for example, he might be a general physician with an interest in cardiology (heart disease) or a general surgeon with an interest in bowel disease. Most consultants are aware of the limitations of their knowledge and will cross-refer if they feel the patient has a condition that falls outside their own competence but within that of a colleague. In the case of a complex and difficult illness the consultant will share the care with other consultants; for example, a diabetic patient with chronic kidney failure and fractured neck of femur (broken hip) will come under the care of a diabetologist, an orthopaedic surgeon, a nephrologist and an anaesthetist. If a patient is admitted to an Intensive Care Unit he could come under the care of five or six consultants, but there will be one consultant responsible for overall management. Every patient is entitled to know under whose care he is and is entitled to see him.

Certainly if the patient is puzzled or unhappy about any aspect of his treatment then he must contact his consultant and explain his worries. You can write to your consultant or, if you are a hospital in-patient, ask the ward staff when you can see him.

On average a consultant is appointed to the post aged between 36 and 40 years. He has been training approximately 20 years to become a consultant. Consultants are usually at their best between the ages of 40 and 55 when experience and new expertise combine for optimum performance. Some consultants are still brilliant when they retire at 65. Consultants are not responsible for domestic services or standards of nursing though they do have an influential input.

The Junior Doctor Team
The Senior Registrar
Surprising as it may seem, all hospital doctors unless they are consultants are called juniors. A senior registrar will usually have been in training 12 to 14 years. As he is coming to the end of his specialist training, he will, on the whole, be as capable as the consultant for whom he works as understudy. He will spend some of his time doing special courses and research. He will work a 50 hour week, plus being on call.

The Registrar
The equivalent of a middle manager, he exercises most responsibility by being the most senior man when the team is 'on call' out of hours in managing emergencies. Although highly competent he does have limitations in his skills and will call in either the senior registrar or the consultant for the management of complex problems. He will have higher qualifications, such as Member of the Royal College of Physicians (MRCP) or Fellow of the Royal College of Surgeons (FRCS), but he will not have advanced special training. He will work a 50 hour week plus being on call. In the near future, the titles of Senior Registrar and Registrar will be merged into one training grade, making the level of training more difficult to discern.

The Senior House Officer
He may have completed the first part of specialist exams but he is now learning most of the procedures and practical skills. The registrar and senior registrar are relatively long term appointments with the team but the SHO changes firms and specialities every six months. Some SHOs will be training in a particular speciality as well as doing their SHO jobs and others will be doing it as part of their

GP training. SHOs can have been qualified for as little as 14 months. He will work a 50 to 80 hour week.

The House Officer
A houseman has passed his medical school final exams and comes to this job before being fully registered with the General Medical Council. He will spend six months as a house physician and six months as a house surgeon. He is highly supervised and his experience is extremely limited; he has just finished being a medical student. The house officer carries out routine, repetitive tasks. He is probably your first point of contact on the ward and you will probably see more of him than any other doctor. He will work a 50 to 80 hour week.

Practical Guidelines
In real terms only a registrar and above should be valued as an opinion on the outcome and management of your case. In order to obtain valid, informed consent for any major operative procedure, it requires the explanation of a registrar or senior registrar or consultant. For routine, non-urgent surgery the patient (if over 16 years of age) should give their own consent. For children under 16, parental consent is necessary. In emergency situations, if the patient is capable, the patient should do so. If the patient is incapable due to mental illness or to the severity of his injuries, for example, if he is unconscious or on a ventilator, then, where time permits, consent should be sought from the nearest relative. In an emergency, for example, in the case of the acutely injured where no consent is available, doctors can proceed with treatment. Where a person is mentally ill or incapable of consent, relatives may give consent or various formal procedures may be instituted on the patient's behalf. If parents with sick children withhold consent inappropriately, consent may, in some circumstances, be sought from the courts.

In practical terms, the day to day work is done by the houseman and the SHO under direction. Any major change of treatment should only be ordered by the senior registrar or registrar. The way the team works is that the consultant initiates the treatment, usually after having seen the patient in outpatients, and then he oversees it in a consultative role, using the ward rounds to make medical management decisions. All teams are structured in a similar way.

The average district general hospital will contain the following consultant teams: around five teams of general surgeons with a range of interests, usually including bowel, breast, and vascular (blood vessel) surgery; five teams of orthopaedic surgeons dealing with disorders of the musculo-skeletal system and some independent teams of surgical sub-specialities like neuro (brain), urology (waterworks), ear, nose and throat, facial and maxillary (jaw) and plastic.

It will have a major obstetrics and gynaecology department covering women's diseases, pregnancy (both normal and abnormal), infertility, abortion, contraception and sterilisation. The obs and gynae consultants in this country cover both specialities and are both physicians and surgeons.

The general medical consultants will have interests in heart problems, lung problems, bowel disease, strokes, tumours and neoplastic disorders (cancers). The medical sub-specialities will include diabetes (blood sugar), rheumatology (bone and joint disorders), long-term chest diseases, asthma, nephrology (kidney) neurology (nervous disorders), gastro-enterology (stomach), and endocrinology (special hormone disorders). Specialised departments of oncology and radiotherapy are found in many hospitals for the treatment of various cancers. Highly specialised units dealing in rarer cancers and children's cancers are found at supraregional centres of excellence.

There will be a department of geriatric medicine specialising in the medical condition of old age but overlapping with every other speciality in the hospital. The management of mental illness and personality disorders in the elderly is handled by consultants specialising in Psychogeriatric Medicine.

Part of your local hospital may be devoted to the treatment of the mentally ill. Usually there will be doctors specialising in the treatment of psychiatric problems in different age-groups, childhood, adolescence and old age. The management of these types of patients takes place, nowadays, mainly in the community, with the use of social workers, community nurses, local GPs and outpatient follow-up. In my experience, although the reasoning behind the concept of Care In The Community is good, lack of investment has led to the overburdening of GPs and a strain on community resources. If a member of your family has a psychiatric illness you will have to fight extra hard to get satisfactory treatment, not because of medical indifference but because it is an area of medicine where people are hard pressed and struggling to make do with the limited resources of time, money and few trained personnel.

Finally, each hospital has an array of important laboratory and technical support services whose findings aid diagnosis. Examples are: Microbiology — the investigation of infective organisms; Cytology — the investigation of cell forms; Histopathology — the investigation of bodily tissues; Biochemistry — the investigation of bodily substances; Haematology — the investigation of blood samples. Radiology can be added to these; however, radiologists not only investigate but also manage diseases, often avoiding the need for surgery.

Staff

Nursing: the Director of Nursing Services is, as the title implies, the person responsible for the quality and standard of nursing in the hospital. This is not a responsibility of the consultants, although they have an influence here. The NHS is highly labour intensive and eighty per cent of the hospital budget is dedicated to staff costs. Over the last few years, in order to contain costs, hospitals have cut back considerably on nursing staff. However, the operators of the new internal market are in danger of overlooking the vital role that nurses play in the healing process. It is said that doctors stop you dying but nurses make you better. Nurses are essential to the comfort of your stay and the long term outcome of your treatment. If you have a complaint about your nursing care, most problems can usually be put right with a word to the ward sister in charge, just as, if you are unhappy with the quality of the food or the standards of cleanliness — the hotel side of the hospital — you should complain to a nursing sister before asking to see someone further up the management tree, be that the duty administrator or the directorate business manager. Hospitals are structured like any other service organisation with acknowledged complaints procedures for service users.

The Government is attempting to develop "the hospital at home" concept, where patients are discharged early and cared for by their GP and community services; the concept is still in its early stages and whether it can work remains to be seen. Certainly, the role of the nurse giving care in the hospital environment cannot be overestimated. I think it is unlikely that there are sufficient GPs and nurses in the community to manage widespread early discharge. Cutting the numbers of expensive hospital beds and nurses may make economic sense to Trust hospitals and increase their viability but it will transfer an expensive burden to the community where the number of GPs is limited and resources may be inadequate to take on extra work without extra funding. The Government faces a dilemma here, since it has said that the central plank of the new reforms is that the money follows the patient but, if that is the case, and the money follows the patient to the community, it will mean a reduction in the money available for hospital services. It is an attractive notion to have people looked after in their home environment but I fear the cost in terms of the diminution of either hospital or community services will be too high.

Persons In Training

Both medical and nursing teams may have students attached to them. They should identify themselves to you as such. They must always ask permission before examining you and be supervised at all times by a suitably qualified person. Not many of us would mind a small amount of discomfort, say the insertion of a drip, to help a student gain valuable experience, but you must be satisfied that student practice is relatively innocuous and will not produce any long term damage. It is not advisable to allow a student to try out his injection technique if you have only one vein available. Furthermore, the fact that you are in a teaching hospital does not mean that your body is available as a learning aid. Before students can do anything to you permission should be sought and consent freely given, otherwise, in law, the actions performed will constitute an assault. Here, as in every other area of medicine Hippocrates' rule applies: "First, do no harm."

Doctors And Nurses As People

Doctors and nurses are people of goodwill who train very hard and work long hours for the privilege of caring for the sick. With very few exceptions, they have the interests of the patient at heart and are prepared to fight for their health service. For many hospital doctors and nurses it is very difficult to be critical of the way their Trust hospital is run and not put their jobs in jeopardy, as many Trusts have a "gagging" clause as part of their employment contract. Since doctors and nurses have a moral and ethical code which overrides their duties to the Trust (their employer), many still choose to take that risk and speak out when they see something that breaches their code. It is important for doctors and nurses to be able to speak out, if necessary, on their patients' behalf as an advocate. For example, if a patient is being deprived of essential treatment. The public needs to support doctors and nurses who speak out. Whistleblowing, when all other avenues have been exhausted, is a necessary right and a moderating influence on employers and Trusts.

As with all authority figures, we often forget doctors and nurses are human like ourselves. Like us they are members of society, with spouses and families and outside interests. Their overriding duty to their patients means they often neglect these but that does not diminish their importance to them. They have personalities with likes and dislikes and a varying ability to get on with people. Although it is unlikely that you will get on well with every doctor and nurse you meet, medicine and nursing are caring professions and so you should be able to establish a viable relationship with most.

To make allowances for doctors and to see them as fully human, subject to the same moods and prejudices as their fellow men, is something we can quite easily do whilst we enjoy good health. However, illness is complex and has unpredictable physical and emotional consequences, where pain and loss of function can distort our perceptions and undermine our sense of worth. Most doctors know this and know that different people react to illness in different ways, often seeming to undergo a personality change in the process that lasts no longer than the illness itself.

Doctors have to deal with a wide variety of personality types and varying degrees of reaction to illness. What kind of patient are you? Where on the spectrum do you stand? We all know people at the one extreme, who never admit they are ill and who refuse to consult a doctor or take to their beds, and people at the other extreme, where even the slightest twinge is seen by them as possibly fatal and who constantly consult their doctors with a whole catalogue of imaginary ills. The doctor has to be aware that this type is unable to cope with life and with themselves and that being a hypochondriac does not protect a person from disease. Even though the doctor may have mentally labelled a patient a "time-waster", a "nut" or someone who cries wolf, known in the profession as "heart-sink" patients, he still has a duty to carry out a full investigation of their alleged complaint. Skilled doctors get a great deal of satisfaction from improving the lot of "difficult patients".

Confidentiality

As a patient you now have a right to see anything that is written about you. Doctors are, therefore, very careful not to write anything that they cannot substantiate if called upon. Doctors do communicate with each other, and it is essential and in your best interests that they do. It is reasonable to allow this to happen so long as the content of their communication is objective, factual and beneficial to you. No doctor in the NHS would knowingly present inaccurate information to a colleague: it wastes his time and may put the patient's life at risk. In order to see your GP notes, ask the GP who may charge a small fee for the service. To see your hospital notes you write to the Unit General Manager with your request. The Unit General Manager will delegate the task to a member of his staff who will contact the relevant consultant who will agree to the release of information to you. You may in some circumstances require the services of a solicitor and obviously you must give your written consent. There are clearly defined rules laid down relating to requests of various types.

However, the central act of medicine will always remain the doctor-patient relationship, and confidentiality is at the core of that relationship. Doctors spend a lot of time observing and protecting confidentiality: it is a central tenet of their professional code. In an environment where patients are seen as commercial objects, as clients or customers, where records are computerised and where hospital and practice managers are seeking more and more control over medical procedures, it is in all our interests to see that confidentiality, as a value and as a right, is vigorously adhered to.

Practical point
Make sure your confidentiality is maintained.

The Right To Know
It is an interesting but strange phenomenon that the doctor-patient relationship stays confidential until the patient is found to be terminally ill. Then the doctors and nurses, for some unexplained reason, tend to inform the relatives and withhold the diagnosis from the patient.

Even when doctors and nurses seek to explain they have a vocabulary all their own which can exclude the patient. If you are being given information about your condition, do not be ashamed to ask for an explanation in plain language. There is a temptation to ask someone, say a student nurse, just because they are easy to talk to, but who is not really suitable. Ask the consultant, especially if you sense you might be suffering from something serious.

Until recently doctors used to refer to "neoplasm" or "growth" when they meant cancer. It used to amaze me at one particular hospital where I was training that, when patients who had a "growth" were told that someone in the same ward, who they knew to have had a "growth" likewise, had died of cancer, they never related the two terms. This form of benevolent paternalism is increasingly rare. The trend now is to tell the patient fully what their prospects are. However, the truth is that some patients would rather not be told and some people are told too quickly and too brutally, or in too unpalatable a way.

One of the real skills of doctoring is telling patients what they want to know by allowing them to ask for as much or as little information as they need at that particular time. Sadly, the telling of bad news is often delegated to the most junior team member. In an ideal world bad news would be given by the most senior person available, with adequate time and privacy and with opportunity for follow-up discussion.

Even a long discussion is too short when it is your terminal illness. Pressure of work and shortage of time often lead to less than ideal communication. This may cause misery for the patient and his/her family and, unfortunately for all concerned, this unhappiness can continue long after the patient is dead. Regrettably the new NHS is more interested in the speed and rate of processes than in measuring the quality of doctoring and nursing. As I said earlier, do not leave it all to the doctors and nurses. You need to know in advance what you want to ask; you need to ensure all problems are explained and that you understand all the answers. Very few doctors have the knack of simplifying complex terminology into the language of the non-medical person; help them by indicating any lack of understanding on your part.

Just as most women, before they enter hospital to give birth, have a birth-plan — that is a clear idea of what is going to happen and the possible complications that might arise — so before entering hospital yourself, find out what your treatment plan is so that you know the range of possible outcomes. If your condition could turn out to be terminal, arrange to be told before your family, or, if that is your way, express the wish that you are not to be told.

Practical point
Make it clear to the team of doctors and nurses looking after you what your views are about keeping your relatives informed and your views on resuscitation and your views, if appropriate, on organ donation. Make sure you have made a will. It is important when you are terminally ill, if you are able to contemplate your end, to discuss

whether you wish to be subject to resuscitation procedures, which can be fairly aggressive, if your heart should stop. Many people wish to die with dignity without the attentions of the cardiac arrest team. It is critically important that the hospital and your relatives clearly understand your wishes. It is not inappropriate for you or your relatives to discuss with your consultant what your wishes are. When a terminal illness has been diagnosed, the patient should consider carefully where he wishes to die. The options are: at home, in the hospital or in a hospice. Discussion with the GP, with family and with the consultant will allow the patient to make up his mind. Many people would like to die at home but do not discuss it with their family. If the patient wishes to die at home then he should tell the consultant, tell his family and arrange to be discharged and for a GP follow-up at home.

Hospitals are formal organisations with rules and procedures. On the one hand this formality, with its direction and sense of purpose, can be a source of comfort and reassurance, and on the other, it can seem intimidating and impersonal with routines often appearing more important than patients. I hope, in this chapter, I have dispelled much of the mystery surrounding who does what in the modern hospital. In the next chapter, I will familiarise you with those common practices and procedures, from admission right through to discharge, that are nowadays part and parcel of hospital life. In this way I hope to remove any fear you may have of feeling awkward and unrehearsed for your new role as hospital patient.

6.

A Survivor's Guide To
Life On The Ward

Admission to hospital can feel very threatening. We experience a loss of control as we exchange the familiar environment of our own home and our own bed for a dormitory of strangers whose only common bond with us is illness. Like them our illness may make us feel vulnerable, threatening our self possession, our dignity and our future competence. No one regards admission into hospital as good news, not even when, as a result, we will be relieved of the burden of our disease, have our pain taken away and the prospects of a long, healthy life restored. And it is even worse news for anyone whose entry into hospital heralds a sequence of admissions for a steadily worsening condition.

However, without dwelling on our morbidity and mortality, and the kind of intimate details that give doctors and nurses themselves a particular dislike of going into hospital as patients, this chapter will rehearse the likely sequence of events you will encounter from the time you enter the hospital doors to the moment of your discharge. Hospitals are full of routines, designed for the smooth running of a complex organisation but also designed to reassure the patient through the continuity, stability and orderliness they give hospital life. I will now preview these routines to help you retain that precious feeling of personal control and to remove the stress of the unfamiliar.

Admission
There are three types of admission. The first is when you refer yourself or are taken to the Accident and Emergency Department who then admit you to the hospital; the second is when your GP gets you admitted under the care of the "on take" team; and the third is when a consultant decides you need hospital treatment or

investigation, after having seen you in Outpatients. It is this last type of admission I shall be dealing with in this chapter as an example, as it contains elements of all the other types of admission procedure.

I have previously urged you not to go into hospital with any lingering uncertainties as to what is going to be done to you, how it is going to be done and why. Make sure, too, that you understand the range of outcomes of your treatment or investigation. As I said in previous chapters, the best time to do this is when you first see the consultant in Outpatients. Otherwise you can discuss further details of your admission procedure with your GP when he receives a letter from the consultant after your outpatient appointment.

After it is decided that you need to go into hospital for treatment or further investigation you will receive in the post a date for your admission and, ideally, an admissions pack which will detail where and when to report and what to bring with you. In general, you will be advised to bring a change of nightwear and a dressing gown and slippers or a tracksuit. You will not have much storage space so cut down on what you bring with you. If you expect a long stay, you can take a portable television if it has an earpiece. Similarly you can take a personal stereo/radio but not without an earpiece. Do not take potted plants as they harbour insects. Hospitals are not secure places so do not take valuables, credit cards or large sums of money. If you are not in a position to leave such items behind then the hospital will put them in a safe and issue you with a receipt, either on admission or, with personal items such as wrist watches and rings, before you go to theatre. Also remember that all hospitals have strict no smoking policies because they consider smoking to be both a health and a fire risk. These days visiting does not have too many restrictions although it is not encouraged on the day of an operation. If possible, it is wise to arrange some kind of informal rota so that people do not all turn up at the same time and that you get to see those that are most important to you most often. Visiting can be tiring and stressful for both the patient and the visitor. Ask the nurses to draw the curtains about your bed to allow some privacy.

Cancellation

Hopefully you have been given a fixed date. However, cancellations can occur if a patient is admitted who is deemed to have a condition more acute than yours. If this happens you have a right to know why your admission was cancelled and when you can next expect to present yourself at the hospital.

In the meantime be aware that your own needs may change and your condition worsen. If you think this has happened to you, go to your GP and if he confirms your observation, get him to inform the consultant by telephone of your new, more urgent present state.

The best way to ensure you get an early admission, right from the start, is to ask the consultant, when he tells you of his decision to admit you, that you would like to be a short-notice list patient. To do this you will need to leave a contact number, have your bag packed and be ready to go as soon as you receive the call. As a short-notice list patient you benefit by securing a bed early, and the hospital benefits by keeping its resources in continuous use. When a bed becomes available the hospital will try your number only once. If they receive no reply they will move on to the next person on the list.

Make sure that your GP appreciates the full effects of your illness. Discuss with him the degree of pain you are suffering, whether it is affecting your employability and what the economic consequences on your life are; for example, a hernia is a more serious condition for someone who has to do heavy-lifting at work than it is for a bank clerk. How many dependants do you have? An elderly lady with a crippled husband and a disabled son would merit being moved further up the queue. Sell your need to the doctor so that he can make a case for you and present a picture of you not just as a diagnosis but as a person in society.

Also make sure that you have described fully all your symptoms and the full extent of your problems. For instance, problems arising from dislocated joints will not kill you but will cause enough pain and discomfort to make their treatment a more urgent necessity. For conditions such as bowel tumours and womb tumours, which are life-threatening, you need an operation sooner rather than later.

If your condition changes significantly get re-prioritised. If your treatment for pain relief is failing, then ask to have it reviewed by being referred to a consultant. If you have angina and your chest pain is getting worse, don't just endure it; go to your GP and get an immediate referral. Do not be afraid to be your own advocate and don't be afraid to explain changes in your condition to your GP.

If you have a common problem and you have been given a long-term appointment, ask your GP to review waiting times for other consultants so that you can be re-referred. GPs are reluctant to do this but it may encourage yours to get you the right referral at the first attempt! You can also ring the National Helpline, 0800 665544,

10 am — 5 pm, Mon. — Fri., a free information service which gives the waiting times in your area.

Getting Onto The Ward

Admissions follow set procedures. When you are called you will be told to go to the Admissions Desk. It is here that there will begin a routine you will need to get used to; otherwise it may become a source of some irritation. This is only the first request for personal details. Because hospitals are large undertakings with lots of coming and going, it is essential there are no mix-ups. Your stay will therefore be punctuated by a variety of people asking for your particulars again and again. I'm afraid that this is unavoidable, but remember it is essential for the safe, careful conduct of the hospital and that the interests of all the patients lie behind it.

After your basic documentation has been checked through at the Admissions Desk and your notes are seen to be all present and correct, you will be directed to your allocated ward. On arrival you can expect to be met in a friendly, helpful manner by a member of the ward staff. You will normally be shown to your bed and advised what to do next. If in doubt, ask. You will also be given a wrist label stating your name, age, date of birth, hospital number, consultant and ward. At some point, you will be seen by a named nurse responsible for your nursing care throughout your stay. This is a new concept promoted in the Government's Patient's Charter and designed to provide you with a person you can relate to throughout your stay. It is a good idea in theory but takes no account of the fact that nurses work in shifts of thirty seven and a half hours and then hand over to others. So, by all means, look out for that friendly familiar face, but do not be disappointed if it is absent for long periods.

When you are settled on the ward, you will be asked for more personal details. These questions will be more extensive, asking about your family and social circumstances and any problems that the hospital should know about which might affect you during your stay. Any dietary restrictions or religious stipulations will also be noted. Do not hesitate to talk to the nurse about the hospital and what you can expect and anything that might be puzzling you.

Clerking

The houseman from the team that is looking after you will now come along to review your medical problems. He will inquire about your past medical history, social circumstances and medication and ask you questions about every system of your body. He will give you a full and detailed examination, followed, perhaps, by a chest x-ray, ECG (visual measurement of your heart rhythm) and various blood tests. This is known as "working up" and its main purpose is to determine your physical state since you attended Outpatients and before you attend theatre, so that nothing is left to chance. Clerking is an opportunity, too, for you to get an update on what is being planned for you. The houseman will write you up for any medication that you are taking on a regular basis and any medication you might need whilst you are in hospital. You will now probably be left alone for a period of time until you are visited by the consultant and his team prior to your operation. It is vital to mention *all* medications you have taken recently, as well as conditions from which you may suffer, even though to yourself these matters may seem unrelated to your particular operation. The doctors must be in a position to know, for example, that some life-threatening reaction, say to an anaesthetic, is a possibility.

Informed Consent
At some point before your operation you will be asked to sign a consent form. It is your right to know what is going to be done, why and by whom. You should also be told what the alternatives are and what the expected outcomes will be of the different methods of treatment. It is sometimes necessary to give consent for eldery relatives who, through age or disease have become incompetent to manage their own affairs. In the event of a serious injury to a member of your family, rendering them unconscious and unable to give consent, you may be asked to give consent as next-of-kin. Make sure you know the full implications and that your consent is truly informed.

Everything in medicine is a balance of risk and benefit. You should be left in no doubt as to what the risks of the procedures are. There is an element of risk in all procedures. This is true of the operative procedures, the anaesthetic procedures, and even in investigative procedures. For instance, in a coronary angiography, where a very fine tube is inserted into the arteries supplying the heart muscle and x-ray dye is squirted in in order to outline the vessel, the fine tube itself may itself completely block an artery, leading to a minor or major heart attack.

Once you know the risks then you are in a position to weigh them up against the possible long term benefits. You have to decide how the short term pain, inconvenience and suffering incurred in your treatment measure up against the long term gains of improved quantity and quality of life. Some people, for instance, would be happy to accept a one-in-five chance of dying if the outcome is five years of pain-free life. Each one of us is prepared to balance risk and benefit individually but this can only be done by informed consent. In other words, you can only make these choices if you have sufficient facts. Doctors have a duty to give the facts in an acceptable manner without necessarily expecting you to have been to medical school and read the definitive text. It is accepted in law that a doctor has to give enough information so that the patient can make an informed choice, without necessarily presenting all the rare risks that may have occurred at some time, somewhere in the world.

If you feel you have been fully informed and are happy with the information, then you can sign your consent form to allow the doctor to operate on your body, on your behalf, within clear limits. Do remember that a doctor has a duty to carry out essential life-saving procedures without your consent in an emergency. The old fashioned consent forms where you signed for an operation without knowing what it was and without naming the surgeon, just allowing the operation to proceed, have long since disappeared. Modern consent forms should be very specific and include both specific wishes and specific exclusions. For instance, you might consent to a lumpectomy but not a mastectomy, that is to say the removal of part but not the whole of a breast. Even for an exploratory operation, there should be agreed procedures for when the surgeon has opened you up. Finally, if you do not understand the consent form and its implications, do not sign it till you do. You may prefer to have a friend, relative or other advisor at your side when you make your decision; if so, it is well to plan such arrangements early.

Any patient has a right to discharge himself at any time, unless admitted compulsorily under the Mental Health Act, but this may be against the advice of his doctors. If you wish to discharge yourself, let the ward sister and the doctors taking care of you know that you wish to do this. They will come along and discuss the matter with you and advise you of the risks of leaving and the possible consequences. If you still wish to leave, you will be asked to sign a "Discharge Against Advice Form" which explains that you are discharging yourself entirely at your own risk. If you sign then you have no comeback against the hospital.

Before Your Operation

Before your operation you will be visited by senior members of the operating team. The visit will be to have you sign the consent form, to mark out the operation site, and to review your notes and the considered findings of the houseman to see if there is any change in your condition. You will be told how you are going to be prepared for the operation, what will happen in the operation and what your likely period of recovery will be. If you are admitted for investigation, then the nature of each investigation will be explained and its implications discussed. You will also be visited by the anaesthetist, a very important man because your life will be literally in his hands during the operation. He may prescribe pre-medication, prior to your anaesthesia, which will help you to feel more relaxed. He will explain the anaesthetic procedures and the inherent risks and talk to you about the vitally important post-operative analgesia (pain relief), which may be carried out in a variety of ways. You may expect to suffer some discomfort, but never prolonged or severe pain or discomfort if your pain-relief regime is properly managed.

At this point you will be left alone on the ward in the care of the nursing staff, having been deluged with information. A nurse will visit you and you can discuss your concerns with her. If she cannot answer your queries, ask her to call back a doctor to see you. Be aware that some nurses have limited knowledge, particularly students and temporary staff. Conversely, some of the more senior staff on the nursing team are very knowledgeable and experienced.

Nurses will now carry out the pre-operative or pre-investigative procedures required, such as preparations of the bowels and pre-operative shaves. You might also be visited by the theatre staff, and if it's a big operation by staff from the Intensive Care Unit (ICU) to explain what is going to happen. You might also be taken to the ICU beforehand to acquaint you with the set-up there. Do not be frightened of asking questions and be sure that you understand the answers.

It is reassuring to know that only necessary procedures are nowadays carried out and that many of the old rituals have been reviewed; only unavoidable unpleasantness now takes place. For example, women who were routinely subject to a pubic shave on the gynaecological ward, now undergo a pubic tidy and only necessary hair is removed. Bowel preparations and enemas are limited.

Now the countdown to the operation begins. You will be given your pre-operative medication and starved of food and drink. You will be advised to shower and given a theatre gown, hat and pants to put on afterwards. Your nail varnish will be removed to see how well oxygenated you are, and your rings will be removed or taped. Undoubtedly this is a time of anxiety for you but with caring and empathetic doctors and nurses and a clear understanding of the likely outcome on your part, anxiety can be reduced to a minimum. Fear of the unknown creates stress; an informed patient with insight is less anxious.

As you leave the ward you will be checked out by having to answer more questions. Who you are, where you are going, for what operation, whether your dentures have been removed. Your wrist label will be checked and you will then be transferred onto a trolley and wheeled down to theatre, feet first. Children are taken to theatre in a variety of imaginative ways, including self-drive electric pedal cars and trolleys resembling locomotives in children's books.

When you get to theatre you will be carefully checked in, which means answering more questions and having your wrist label checked, as the ward nurse hands over to the anaesthetic theatre nurse who will then introduce herself. ECG pads are then attached to your chest so that your heart traces can be checked. The anaesthetist will now approach and identify himself. He will then either put a mask over your face or insert a needle in your vein. Whatever the method of anaesthesia, you will attain, almost instantaneously, the complete oblivion necessary for the surgeons to carry out their task.

After The Operation

If the anaesthetic has worked properly you are unlikely to remember anything until you wake up again on the ward. You may have a sore nose and throat from where a tube was inserted during the operation and some discomfort from the site of your operation. But ideally there should be no pain, as the pain will be taken care of by the post-operative analgesics prescribed by the anaesthetist and administered by the nursing staff. Speed of recovery varies from person to person so do not feel embarrassed if yours is taking longer than anticipated. Only go home when you are good and ready and when the necessary domestic support services, whose arrangement should have been discussed with you on admission, are in place.

You will be visited daily by doctors checking on your progress and by the consultant on his ward round. A good consultant will visit you the day after your operation, and prior to your discharge.

Similarly, a good anaesthetist will visit soon after the operation to assess pain control. Again, if you have any queries, ask. It is a point I have stressed over and over again in this book: it is better to have an informed mind rather than a troubled one. Like all people who have mastered a technical subject, doctors sometimes find it difficult to remember the time when they were just as ignorant as everybody else.

Nursing Staff

In the period after your operation or investigation the nursing staff become very important to you. They are there to aid your recovery and help you regain your strength. Each ward is run by a ward sister with overall responsibility for the ward. Each department, too, has a senior nurse in charge. Nurses, like the doctors, work in different areas of medicine and so will have their own appropriate qualification for that area. The nursing staff work within a grading system and each nurse has a grade related to qualifications. Different types of nurses have different uniforms which will vary from hospital to hospital. Student nurses will also play a supervised role as they gain practical experience. Hospitals are also staffed by Healthcare Assistants who are part of a national vocational training scheme. They have very little formal training and learn their tasks on the ward, being instructed by members of the ward team. The trend in Trust hospitals is, with the idea of saving costs, to rely more and more on Healthcare Assistants to nurse the patients and less on trained nurses.

Other than on minor matters, it is wise only to take advice from trained personnel. On the entrance to every ward there should be a photographic record of ward staff so this should help you identify the ward sister and the staff nurses. However, since nurses work a shift system, each shift comprising eight hours, and some are part-time, it is difficult to predict when individual nurses will be present to take care of you.

Post-operatively, you may be offered the services of a physiotherapist, a dietitian and an occupational therapist according to your need. Social workers are also available, if required.

Discharge

The discharge from hospital is part of your care and should be planned as such, starting when you are admitted into the hospital. Where possible you should go home with a plan. You should know when you are next expected to attend Outpatients and what the likely course of your illness will be over the next couple of days. You should have a letter for your GP and, if required, some medication, although the hospital will only supply enough for two or three days. It is vitally important, therefore, that you take your discharge letter to your GP as soon as possible to get the full course of medication that may be essential and maintain the continuity of care. If you have had an operation then the procedure for wound-care should be explained before you leave. This may include visiting your local healthcare centre or being referred to a District Nurse, or going back to the hospital, to have the wound tended and the dressings changed. In due course the hospital will send a full and detailed summary of your treatment to your GP.

Do not leave hospital with any unanswered questions. You must have a clear idea of what is going to happen in the future in terms of follow-up. If you were in for an investigation, for instance, do you know when your results are expected and when you should attend the hospital to be told?

For most people a visit to the hospital is a rare occurrence, a landmark event in their lives. They enter hospital as a novice patient, inexperienced, unprepared and a little bewildered. This chapter has rehearsed the likely events that will occur during your stay and hopefully will have prompted in you suitable questions and behaviour so that you will be at ease, especially in the circumstances of the new NHS. In the last chapter we saw that doctors and nurses are people of goodwill with the interests of the patient at heart, who train very hard and work long hours in caring for the sick. They are also human, working in an imperfect organisation. Errors occur and there are lapses in standards; however, normally, they are not on any large scale or to such an extent that you should feel unduly alarmed at the prospect of visiting your GP or of going into hospital. The next chapter tells you what to do if you think you have not had the treatment you deserve or you believe that you are the victim of medical negligence.

*Practical point
Where a relative is a patient in a ward, particularly if elderly, feel free to discuss their care and condition with the medical and nursing staff. If you are concerned about the standard of care, discuss it with the ward staff. Remember, on some wards three nurses may be looking after thirty difficult elderly patients. Offers of practical help

from relatives are often gratefully received. Many wards are badly understaffed and the nurses are doing their best under very trying circumstances. Unhelpful criticism is one more added pressure. We are all familiar with the difficult elderly relative and you have to consider that your relative may be making life difficult for the nurses. Old people removed from their home environment can become confused and disoriented. On the other hand, some can be attempting to manipulate their relatives and ward staff for their own ends.

Under recent legislation, hospitals are not allowed to discharge patients until appropriate discharge arrangements have been made with the community. Trusts are aiming for ever shorter lengths of stay and are effectively rationing the use of beds for the elderly. Appropriate arrangements for community care must be made before the patient is discharged. Since April 1, 1993, patients have been referred to social services if they need social care. There should be full involvement of the GP, too, before discharge.

Many families may be surprised at the level of financial contributions expected from their elderly relative in order to provide residential care in a nursing home. Do not expect the NHS to provide entirely for your elderly relative as of now, and expect even less for yourself in the future. Do not blame doctors, nurses or social workers for this. This is Government legislation which penalises those who have been saving throughout their lives and presently allows the spendthrift off scot-free — a matter for public debate at the political level. According to recent draft guidelines if you have more than £8,000 in assets you will have to pay the full cost of your long-term care. Once savings have been exhausted, children can find they have to sell their parents' home to continue paying the charges. Full-time nursing care costs £22,500 per year in south-east England and £17,500 per year elsewhere.

Practical point
Should you be considering insurance for your own care in extreme old age?

Notes For Parents
Everything said about adult referral and hospital organisation applies to children as well, except that you are encouraged to be with your children as much as you can, even to the point of accompanying them as far as the anaesthetic room prior to any major procedure. There is one other major difference: children under the age of sixteen

cannot sign the Consent Form. You as an adult must do that, bearing in mind everything I said earlier in the chapter.

Wherever possible you will be welcomed to stay overnight to be available to your young child but remember, too, the importance of caring for your other children at home. Children at home frequently need support and reassurance as well, especially if the disappearance of a brother or sister has been unexpected or in dramatic circumstances.

Hospitals are aiming to provide high quality care for children and many are being very successful. There is, however, a shortage of resources and of skilled Children's Nurses. Some parents may find it difficult to get their children referred to centres of national excellence when their child's illness is rare and resources for referral are limited.

7.

Getting An Answer

The NHS is a vast undertaking. To care for the health of the nation around a million people are mobilised — the largest workforce of any organisation in Europe. This enables, for instance, 90% of all families in the UK to be seen by a GP and 12 million people to be treated by their Accident and Emergency Department each year, throughout the land. For ingrowing toenails as well as heart and lung transplants, the NHS is there to care for every aspect of the nation's health. In the main, this huge task is carried out quietly and competently with the vast majority of users satisfied with their treatment. But with an enterprise of such scale, things do go wrong and mistakes are made, with consequences that can range from mild bureaucratic inconvenience to deep and fatal tragedy. Some problems are avoidable and a few occur because of professional negligence. Some of the avoidable ones seem to occur partly because of the internal markets that have been introduced. Rationing according to the market may be to the advantage of the majority with common problems but it can disadvantage the minority with less common diseases such as rare endocrine disorders and those who are elderly or infirm or less able to describe their ailments successfully and put their own case as forcibly as necessary.

Furthermore, as health issues continue to be publicly aired and attention becomes focused on the norms and standards of NHS service, people are beginning to question more the performance of their GP or their local hospital, measuring them against the criteria the media and the Government produce. So far, most of the measuring is related to processes, such as waiting lists and availability of beds, and not to medical or nursing practices, treatments, techniques or the quality of overall care.

The intention behind many of the NHS reforms is to make it more open and more responsive to the views of its customers. When it comes to registering a complaint, you can benefit from this new attitude if you know where in the NHS you can get your complaint dealt with and what exactly you are seeking when you complain: is it an explanation, an apology, a change in the system or compensation? This chapter will show you how to determine the nature of your complaint and make it effective. The general rule for complaining in any area of life applies here also: always try to resolve your differences with whoever is the direct cause of your complaint before approaching a higher authority. Nevertheless, I am conscious that most people are not looking for an argument but simply seeking an explanation.

If you are going to complain, consider whether your complaint is reasonable and be clear in your own mind what outcome you wish to achieve. Constructive complaints can benefit many people but spurious or facetious complaints waste time and resources; they provoke a great deal of stress and anxiety in the doctors and nurses who are being complained about, with adverse effects on their health, work and families. Remember too that doctors and nurses are frequently working under pressure, and simple failures in communications, on both sides, may be the cause of misunderstanding. Malicious or unjustifiable complaints are against natural justice. A doctor is also a person and justice is due to him as it is to anyone else.

General Practice
Ninety-five per cent of all consultations take place in general practice, so GPs are the source of most complaints. You need to distinguish between problems that are relatively trivial, such as having to wait excessively long for a non-urgent matter, or there not being enough car parking space, or even problems that arise because of a personality difference − for example, that you find the doctor tactless, brusque or insensitive − and problems that are serious, such as failure to make the right diagnosis, prescribing the wrong treatment or not treating at all. Although here, it is wise to remember that, however much doctors try to give the opposite impression, medicine is not an exact science. Diagnosis is frequently difficult and of necessity consists of a process of slow, methodical enquiry, since the doctor has to have the correct diagnosis before he can institute the correct treatment. Time is a great diagnostician; many problems evolve and the answers become clear with time.

You have to determine, first of all, if your grievance might not be due to a simple misunderstanding or breakdown in communication between you and the GP. For example, you might have had your day disrupted by being kept waiting, and not realise it is because the GP has been called out to an emergency. Make an appointment to see him if you feel aggrieved and ask for an explanation. He will probably welcome an opportunity to clear up any misunderstanding. Perhaps a discussion with the practice manager might solve problems to everyone's satisfaction.

Also, with regard to diagnosis, bearing in mind the inexact nature of medicine, the usual course that doctors pursue is to treat common diseases commonly. In other words, some illnesses share the same symptoms in their early stages and so it is prudent practice to treat for the most commonly occurring of those illnesses. If you do not respond to treatment, then the doctor will eliminate his first diagnosis and move on to the next possible diagnosis. A treatment could fail but the doctor's overall diagnostic method may nevertheless be sound with the diagnosis changing as the disease develops.

Doctors do not know everything. If in doubt or baffled, a wise GP will quickly seek a second opinion and should not resent your requesting one if you feel your symptoms are being misinterpreted or wrongly diagnosed. However, if, on the whole, you are dissatisfied with your GP because, for instance, you do not find you have easy access or he fails to answer your questions, or you suspect that he has not kept up to date with his knowledge of medicine, or he refuses to refer you for a second opinion, then by all means change your GP following the guidelines in Chapter 2. Contrary to popular belief, doctors do not blacklist you if you wish to transfer. If you are unable to find another GP, contact your FHSA (Family Health Services Authority — see your local phone book) who will allocate you one. On the other hand your GP could himself arrange for you to be transferred by applying to the FHSA.

In practice very few transfers by either party occur, which could be due to our current satisfaction with our doctors or, alternatively, to a lack of interest in our health. It seems more likely though, that the public generally are unfamiliar with the procedure as well as fearful of the result; and that the feeling is (among those that are fed up), "Well, all doctors are as bad." This thinking does not stand to reason. Line up 10 motor mechanics, 10 vicars, 10 lawyers and ask yourself how many out of each group are likely to be a) first class b) average c) useless? Why should doctors be any different?

Perhaps the criteria for selecting our doctors is wrong. Maybe medicine should not simply choose on the basis of A-level results. The qualities of care, compassion and academic ability are a difficult blend. Research indicates that medicine does select caring people and that their vulnerability to the 4 Ds (Drink, Depression, Drugs and Divorce) suggests that there is, for many of them, a certain lack of concern about their own lives.

Serious Complaints

Even though over half the consultations in General Practice are for "minor", self-limiting illnesses requiring only simple medication, the GP is still faced with major acute, chronic and social problems and has to pass judgment on them daily. Social problems lie behind many of the "ills", real or imaginary, that are brought to the GP. The effects of unemployment, poor housing and the disintegration of the family repeatedly manifest themselves in organic disease states. If you feel that your GP has failed, in your case, to diagnose such a disease when another, competent doctor, faced with the same evidence, would have made a correct diagnosis, then there are several steps you can take. The first would be to approach your local Community Health Council to discuss the matter with them. The Community Health Council exists to represent the public's interest in the way medicine is practised and services are delivered. It consists of lay but trained personnel. They will advise you what to do and may or may not take up your case and follow it through. You can also go to the Citizens Advice Bureau for further advice. In cases of life-threatening, acute illness, the NHS functions well at district hospital level. The problems arise when you are stabilised and advanced treatment is needed, perhaps ITU (Intensive Therapy Unit) care, for example, or neurosurgery or coronary artery surgery.

If, after discussion with these bodies, you feel you have a genuine and provable grievance, then you might go to the FHSA to whom the GP is contracted, and who have a statutory duty to ensure that GPs deliver an appropriate standard of service within clear but very broad guidelines. When you have lodged your complaint, the FHSA may initiate a series of formal procedures which will culminate in a hearing at which your doctor will be asked to account for his actions. If the FHSA is not satisfied with his explanation they have the power to withhold part of his salary when his standard of service falls below par. If the matter is sufficiently serious they could refer it to the General Medical Council, the professional regulatory body for doctors which I will discuss further in this chapter when I deal with hospital complaints. The GMC is not a tribunal run by doctors for doctors; it is an independent body consisting of both professional and lay members. Incidentally, magistrates courts and the police will inform the GMC about criminal offences committed by doctors. No other professional body is subject to this form of surveillance.

If you have suffered serious hurt as a result of your doctor's incompetence or negligence — you have lost earnings, your life has been blighted by avoidable pain or has been predictably shortened, for instance, by him not acting on hospital test results that showed something to be seriously wrong — then you may be entitled to legal redress. There are solicitors that specialise in cases of medical negligence and you would be well advised to involve one at an early stage. But a word of caution: however much you feel aggrieved and however great your sense of justifiable outrage, the legal view is not always the common sense view and there is a possibility you could lose; there is also a possibility that you could win but that your legal costs would exceed your awards. Legal aid is rarely available in these cases and even those on modest incomes will probably have to fund their own cases. We as a society should also remember that when individuals achieve vast awards totalling half a million pounds or more, wards close and services are restricted for the rest of us taxpayers as a direct result.

GPs are responsible for the standard of staff they directly employ, the Practice Manager, and the receptionists. The GP may not be directly responsible for the practice nurses, health visitors and some attached personnel.

Just as in commerce there are customers whom shops and businesses would gladly not entertain, so in medicine there are patients who are unreasonable in their demands and confrontational in their approach, whom doctors would prefer not to have on their list. GPs do try to share the burden of difficult patients among themselves and even with these they are still anxious to do their best, just as they are with the rest of their patients who they prefer to keep.

If you want to take some responsibility for your treatment and share in the decision making with your GP, you need to keep the lines of communication open at all times. If there is something about the practice that troubles you, including the doctor's behaviour, then seek an interview and be clear what you are expecting from the interview. You may be angry, for instance, that he could not see you at the time you wanted. Make up your mind beforehand as to what he can do to assuage your hurt feelings. A reasonable explanation may be all that is required. However, if there is no excuse, then you might find a gracious apology acceptable. On the other hand, you may feel that the delay is due to him operating an inefficient appointments system that makes no distinction between the acutely ill patient needing immediate treatment and those with less urgent long-term problems. Here you would want an assurance that he will modify the system in a way that would benefit you in the future and the other patients as well. The new NHS seeks to be responsive to patients' demands and many practices and hospitals have a suggestions box or book.

Hospital

However, it is well to cultivate your GP and not allow unnecessary misunderstandings to occur, for it is in dealing with hospitals that your GP becomes invaluable to you. Trust hospitals are now competing with each other for patients. Patients are referred by GPs and if he is a fundholder then he purchases the services of the hospital on behalf of his patients directly. If you feel that in your case service has not been delivered properly then the person to see is your GP who, in the new system, has considerable influence. However, if you want to handle the matter yourself, I will now go on to tell you how to negotiate in the new Trust system so that you can get satisfaction.

Every Trust hospital is now run by a Unit General Manager. Sometimes this can be a doctor, more often it is someone with a business or industrial background with managerial and administrative skills. He will work with a group of Directors, including a Medical Director, and between them they are responsible for running the hospital which, in turn, is divided into a series of business units mainly corresponding to the old departments, each with its own Clinical Director, Business Manager and Directorate Nurse as a common model. This means that consultants are no longer autonomous but are responsible to the Director running their particular business unit. Trusts regrettably also have a group of Non-Executive Directors who may have little specialist knowledge and whose aptitude for the job is not always evident. These people are solely "political" appointees, approved by the Secretary of State for Health without open public competition.

If you feel you have grounds for complaint you must decide whether your complaint falls under an "administrative" or under a "medical" heading. For instance, if you are upset by being served poorly prepared food or if a member of staff is rude to you, these are administrative issues. If the ward sister cannot deal with your complaint satisfactorily you can summon the Business Manager of the unit, going up the hierarchy, just as you might, say, when complaining in a department store. If, on the other hand, you have grounds for thinking your consultant is not treating you competently then you can complain to the Director of his unit. If the consultant's junior doctors are not treating you competently, then complain to the consultant. And if you feel dissatisfaction with the standard of nursing, complain to the senior nurse in charge. As a wise move, copy all correspondence to the Unit General Manager. You are entitled first to an acknowledgement of your complaint and then later to a considered reply.

Failure Of Treatment
Before I go on to talk in detail about what to do if you think you are the victim of medical negligence, it is necessary, first of all, to consider other factors which could determine failure of treatment. You have to reflect that failure of treatment could be due more to inadequate resources or factors beyond human control, or to the scope of current medical knowledge, than to individual incompetence. It is no use complaining about the waiting time to have your coronary artery bypass graft, if your region has only one surgeon qualified to perform the operation. This is a national resource problem outside the control of your local doctors. Many decisions that affect the availability of certain services are being made for us by the Government without consultation. The only means of making our views known about these big issues is through our MP and MEP.

Unfortunately, many of our services have been changed both locally and nationally, with far too little consultation. Many of my colleagues in medicine feel that the pace of change is too fast and not necessarily for the greatest common good. While some of the concepts directing change in the new health service may produce efficiency in some of the services, other patient groups are being deprived and the needs of all of society are not being adequately planned for, or addressed. Strategic planning is important in medicine, to protect the inarticulate, the poor, the mentally ill and the elderly.

There are certain core services that need to be provided which are tailored to local needs and wishes. However, the non-executive directors of the Trusts are political appointments and therefore our ability to have our voices heard and to influence decisions is limited. In my view, if we really want to empower patients, we should allow elected members of the local community to have a say in the running of local hospitals and we should reduce accordingly the direct control of the Secretary of State.

The Risks Of Medicine

Remember, too, that every procedure has its risks and that powerful medicines have powerful side effects. Even modern laparoscopic surgery, which is characterised as being quick, neat and stream-lined, involves pressurising the abdomen by pumping it full of gas, and introducing, through a small incision, a telescope which has then to be guided with a lot of educated guesswork into position round various vital organs. No amount of obstetric skill and sophisticated gadgetry will ever eliminate all the dangers surrounding child-birth: the most hazardous episode of our life occurs when we are propelled seven inches down the birth canal into the waiting world. There will always be less than perfect babies in a less than perfect world.

Complications can develop in surgery which cannot be anticipated other than by opening the patient up. Every tummy opened is a Pandora's Box likely to display new disease states undetectable from without.

It is well to remember we have all got to die of something, it is just the method of our death that remains to be determined. When we die, the illness we are struck down with is often not the one to which we finally succumb. What happens is that when one bodily system fails it puts the other systems under duress. Thus, for example, an elderly patient can sustain a broken hip, be prescribed bed rest, but then develop clots in the legs which travel to the lungs causing a pulmonary embolism which leads to the collapse of the respiratory system and death. In spite of there being enormous advances in the treatment and prevention of clots, they still occur. Such a progression may be as unavoidable as it is final. There may well be no question of negligence or error on the part of the hospital. Nature has just taken its course. If we annihilated all human diseases, immortality would not follow; instead we would just see long and lingering deaths. However, rest assured, people working in our hospitals will do all they can to prevent avoidable death.

Claiming Medical Negligence

Some negligence is obvious, such as the wrong operation being performed or the wrong treatment given but in other instances you will need to establish whether the performance of the doctor falls below the commonly accepted standard of the profession. This is a lot more difficult to do. Different standards of practice are expected from different grades of doctors. Furthermore, the "gold standard" of an advanced specialist unit cannot be applied to an underfunded, overworked District General Hospital.

The first step that you can take which makes it easier to establish negligence should it occur is, prior to undergoing any routine, planned item of service treatment or investigation, to make sure you fully understand the Consent Form you sign before anything is done to you. Your consent to treatment or investigation needs to be *informed* consent which, in turn, means having the right expectation of the likely outcome of the procedure and being fully cognisant of all its risks and possible side effects. In reality, your decision is a gamble, assessed on a scale of probability, that the benefits of the procedure will outweigh the risks. Most experienced doctors will paint a worse picture of the possible outcomes than is usually the case, so that the patient does not have unrealistic expectations.

In emergency situations which call for snap decisions, hurried actions, and where consent has frequently to be presumed, it is harder for the patient to establish negligence when something goes wrong. Nevertheless the procedure for getting redress is the same. A doctor is not negligent if his actions are reasonable and would generally match those of a body of his peers, and they are carried out in good faith.

Getting Redress

First of all you have to assemble the facts. To do this you will need to talk to the consultant concerned and get his side of the story. It is as well to know that you are entitled to obtain your case notes but decoding them may be difficult. Do not hesitate to ask your doctors to explain the big words written in your notes. At the present time one has to assume that your notes will be delivered intact. Almost all notes are of the loose leaf type and may not be in a numbered sequence. Alterations should not be made retrospectively, without being dated and initialled. Clearly, this is not a satisfactory situation and is one to which the new customer-oriented NHS needs to give some attention.

If, at this stage, you still feel aggrieved, you will be well-advised to contact your Community Health Council for guidance and at the same time register your complaint with the Unit General Manager of the Trust. Action For The Victims of Medical Accidents (see back of book for phone/address) offer advice and are worth contacting in cases of difficulty. According to the guidelines laid down by the Patient's Charter, every complaint has to be responded to, investigated and a reply sent. If at this stage you do not think you are getting satisfactory answers or that your case is not being treated with the seriousness it merits, then you can report the individual doctor to the General Medical Council (see back of book for phone/address), the medical profession's own regulatory body, either directly or through your local FHSA. The General Medical Council consists of both lay and medical members, and is extremely jealous and protective of the high standards within the medical profession. It deals severely with those whose conduct it considers to have fallen short of these standards. Fortunately, the standards of doctors and nurses are generally excellent.

Individual NHS Trusts do monitor their performance through internal audit. Audit is a system by which performance in the hospital is monitored and systems are changed in order to improve outcomes for the benefits of patients. In each hospital three senior doctors, known as The Three Wise Men, have the task of keeping an eye on their colleagues. Also, each hospital has an Ethics Committee governing the management of new treatments and research. The general public has the added safeguard that the local Coroner always orders a post mortem examination in cases where a patient dies of unexpected causes. Although this is no consolation if you are that patient, nonetheless the knowledge that any careless work could be subject to this kind of close scrutiny acts as a moderating influence on doctors in their day to day activity. Generally, doctors would like a post mortem on all patients who die since doctors are keen to know about disease processes. Unfortunately, many families, for understandable reasons, do not want post mortems on their loved ones. Medical science, future patient care and indeed many relatives would benefit from more post mortems.

Nationally, studies are carried out, such as CEPOD (Confidential Enquiry into Peri-operative Deaths) which scrutinises deaths occurring at or around the time of operation. Remember again, that simply because a death has occurred, does not necessarily mean that the doctors have failed; many heroic operations are destined to fail in spite of the best efforts of all concerned and the deployment of vast sums of taxpayers' resources.

Sudden deaths do occur at all ages where no one is to blame. Deaths and injury occur where the patients themselves are to blame. For example, you can maximise your survival chances if you lose weight, stop smoking and get fit prior to surgery. Your complication rate will be reduced and your chances of survival increased accordingly.

What does give serious cause for concern is the death of the previously healthy who die at operation or shortly afterwards. Unpleasant though it may be for a family to contemplate, a post mortem is often very revealing and a death certificate will give interesting and relevant information; however, you may need to get an explanation of what the medical terminology means by discussing it with your GP.

The issue of apportioning responsibility is one that is set to become more and more crucial. Medicine is carried out by human beings with less than adequate resources in less than ideal conditions. Except where individuals opt to pay, it is generally accepted in this country that it is the Government's responsibility to provide those resources. If the patients die due to lack of resources, then it is unfair to blame individual doctors. It is the Government's decision, on our behalf, exactly how to ration those resources. The emotive question of who is to blame for avoidable deaths is increasingly being asked, though the national discussion where both Government and public agree on what resources should be provided has still to take place. Meanwhile, people of goodwill at local level cannot be held responsible for the consequences of decisions taken at national level.

It is for the Government to decide, on our behalf, how to deploy resources. The resources are limited and even their efficient use cannot prevent rationing. Until there are enough intensive care and paediatric beds in particular, unnecessary deaths will occur. Until there is an appropriate number of cardio-thoracic surgeons, people will die on waiting lists waiting for heart surgery. It is my personal belief that resources should be used efficiently and that the taxpayer should get maximum benefit for each pound spent in the health service. It is also my belief that the public should be involved in the debate over what resources are available, what level of tax is needed to pay for them and where our priorities as a nation lie. We as a nation spend a relatively small percentage of our GNP on health (6.6%).

As yet the new NHS has not faced up to the full implications of medical liability and of who is actually responsible for paying some of the vast damages that can occur, especially when babies are born handicapped. For example, if your local maternity unit has the misfortune to be responsible for the delivery of two or three brain damaged babies in a year they could be faced with a legal judgment of three to four million pounds plus costs against them. This would result in the closure of wards and large numbers of people being deprived of healthcare in order to compensate a few. This is clearly unfair. Maybe Trusts should insure against these losses or, alternatively, a ceiling should be applied to such liability with patients taking out private insurance for added cover, if they so wish, although this would require a change in the law of the land.

The Government has issued two Charters outlining what standards and services we can expect from the NHS. In the next chapter I will examine these Charters and see in what way they can help us obtain the best from current healthcare provision.

8.

Rights And Responsibilities
In A Rationed Heath Service

The explosion of knowledge and technical ability in the last fifty years means that the public demand for healthcare is almost infinite. To meet such a demand would be impossible and therefore, whatever the level of Government spending, there still has to be rationing in some form. Unfortunately we are being encouraged by politicians of all parties into thinking that all treatments are available for all the people all the time. Although such politicians have not got the courage to say so, rationing is happening, currently in the form of an artificial internal market, and will continue to happen under other governments, possibly in different guises. Once you know that rationing is occurring although it has not been made explicit by the politicians, you can take steps to make sure you survive by understanding the new, refashioned health framework.

Take The Right Steps
The single most important thing you can do to make sure you benefit from recent changes in the health service is to choose the right GP. GPs vary in knowledge and interest and in the degree of power they wield in getting you referred. They also differ in the amount of resources such as practical facilities, equipment and funding they have at their disposal. At present, a third of British doctors are fundholders who, besides having good facilities and services, are usually better able to get you a quick referral to the right hospital consultant than their non-fundholding colleagues. Nevertheless, no matter now efficient or slick a doctor may be, if you do not like him as a human being there is not much point in choosing him as your doctor. To receive proper diagnosis and treatment it is essential that you are able to communicate your needs. Before choosing, you must

be convinced that the doctor will take you seriously, that he has time to listen to what you have to say and that he will make an effort on your behalf.

Medicine is many-sided and although family doctors are called *General* Practitioners they do have special interests within the discipline. Thus some are good at dealing with children, some with old people, and some with women's problems. Find a practice that can deal adequately with your particular needs and do not hesitate to change practices when you find that your needs change — when your family grows up, for instance, or if you develop a chronic condition outside the competence of your particular GP.

The transaction between doctor and patient is a two-way process and many of the difficulties arising in general practice stem from patients adding themselves to a doctor's list and neither party giving enough thought to the selection procedure. I have said it is a good idea to interview a GP to whom you might be thinking of changing. It would also save a lot of misunderstanding in many cases, if the doctor, too, made it clear what he expects from a prospective patient.

Your Rights In Respect Of Your GP — The Patient's Charter

In 1992, the Government published its Patient's Charter which outlines what is described as "your basic rights to general medical services and the standards of service you can expect". Each practice is encouraged to develop its own Practice Charter, as well. As a document the Patient's Charter is a good guide to what is right and what is wrong with the present system but it is, perhaps, of only limited use if what you are seeking is the best quality care rather than basic rights and minimum standards. It states twelve basic rights which you have:

- to be registered with a family doctor. Where you are not registered with a doctor your FHSA (Family Health Service Authority — see your phone book) must find you one within two working days.
- to change your doctor easily and quickly.
- to be offered a health check:
  *when joining a doctor's list for the first time
  *if you are between 16 and 74 and have not seen your doctor in the previous three years, and
  *a yearly home visit if you are 75 years old or over.
  (An excellent point. Make sure you use this opportunity.)
- to receive emergency care at any time through a family doctor. (The Charter does not specify what constitutes an emergency. Is

it an emergency, for instance, if someone has not anticipated running out of their supply of medicine? There is potential here for misuse of the system and for waste of taxpayers' money.)

- to have appropriate drugs and medicine prescribed. (At the same time the doctor is under pressure to use the cheapest medicine available and not to prescribe if there is a medicine available that can be bought over the counter.)

- to be referred to a consultant acceptable to you when your family doctor thinks it necessary, and to be referred for a second opinion if you and your family doctor think this is desirable.

- to have access to your health records, subject to any limitations in law. (You may be asked to contribute a small administrative fee for retrieving these.)

- to know that those working for the NHS are under a legal duty to keep the content of your health records confidential. (This is an overriding duty. With the increase of administrative personnel in the new health service, too many people know too much about patients. Only doctors and nurses should get to see the medical bits of NHS records. Anyone else should do so only on a strictly need-to-know basis. You will not be allowed to see the records of another adult unless they are records of a deceased relative and you have a special interest in them.)

- to choose whether or not to take part in medical research or medical student training. (You have a right to know who people are and what they are doing there.)

- to be given detailed information about local family doctor services through your FHSA's local directory.

- to receive a copy of the doctor's practice leaflet, setting out the services he or she provides.

- to receive a full and prompt reply to any complaint you make about NHS services.

Is The Charter Realistic?

I have stressed throughout this book how important it is to build up a good relationship with your GP. My aim in doing this is so that you can have honest and open dealings with your doctor so that *quality* of care is paramount. You are using your doctor as a knowledgeable, highly-trained professional in your quest to stay healthy and make the best of yourself. The Patient's Charter, by stressing your rights with no reference to personal responsibility, prolongs the myth that somehow all medical treatment is free and there is no obligation on our part to make proper use of a precious resource. The Charter does not tell us how to ensure quality of treatment. It does not address those people who call out doctors inappropriately or those who take up valuable appointment time to get for free, those medicines which should be part of every family medicine chest and bought over the counter, or others who continually consult their GP over very trivial self-limiting complaints. All this costs taxpayers' money and is a huge drain on the resources of the NHS — resources that could be used in more vital areas.

The Charter does not disentangle the responsibility of the GP to provide a high quality professional service from the Government's own responsibilities of providing enough resources for the doctors to deliver that service and of providing good strategic management so that everyone gets the same standard of treatment irrespective of their postal code. The Government has to ensure that resources are not wasted on doctors doing administrative tasks rather than diagnosing and treating patients or upon administrators inappropriately building empires.

It does not say how standards are going to be raised all round. Nor does it consider how patients are to be educated about taking responsibility for their own health, nor what the Government is going to do to provide the resources to reduce the packed surgeries and the huge patient demand for GPs' time. I have said that when you visit the doctor to consult over something that concerns you, you should expect the consultation to last a minimum of ten minutes. It is a pity that a quality consultation does not feature in the Patient's Charter as an overriding priority along with a commitment to provide the necessary enabling resources and a spelling out of just what we as individual patients are entitled to in terms of essential treatment.

The Charter does outline our rights but it is within a health service where we as citizens have little say in what services are provided. It is time that central government did a consultation exercise and asked people what they expect from their National Health Service and set an agenda for providing what is possible and realistic.

Complaining

Your best approach — as I have urged — is to seek out a GP with whom you can communicate easily and openly and whose medical expertise you can count on, and not someone about whom you will eventually find yourself making a formal complaint. GPs have an enhanced role in the new health service and your GP will prove a useful ally in gaining the right referral and gaining access to the services of the NHS. He is also a valuable advocate and counsellor if things go wrong.

Nevertheless, the Patient's Charter gives certain undertakings on behalf of your Family Health Service Authority about handling any complaint you might make about your GP or a member of his staff if you are not satisfied in any way with the service they give. It promises that the FHSA, with whom the GP is under contract, will provide a full and open response to any comments, suggestions or complaints which a member of the public makes about those services. It also promises that your FHSA will react promptly to your comments, suggestions and complaints and acknowledge them within two working days and, where appropriate, that it will advise your family doctor of their receipt within the same time limits, and that it will clear informal complaints within one month. Formal complaints they only promise to clear within six months because they are handled within a legal framework. The FHSA will also provide you and your family doctor with monthly progress reports until your complaint has been cleared.

Practical point
The FHSA will only accept a complaint against a doctor if it is within 13 weeks of the incident which is the cause of your complaint, so act promptly. There is further practical guidance about complaining at the end of this book.

The NHS In General

Besides dealing with family doctor services, the Government has also made sure the Patient's Charter looks at a patient's rights and the standards you can expect with regards to the National Health Service in general. It identifies additional National Health Service rights which every citizen has. It is valuable to have these rights made explicit, even if some of them are more aspiration than present NHS reality. Accordingly, this Charter also says you have the following rights:

1. To receive healthcare on the basis of clinical need, regardless of ability to pay. (Bear in mind that it is not always possible to fund the treatment of expensive diseases.)

2. To receive emergency medical care at any time, through your GP or the emergency ambulance service and hospital Accident and Emergency departments.

COMMENT: Irresponsible users of these services are stretching them to breaking point, flooding GPs at night and the Accident and Emergency departments all the time, with trivial problems. The increasing use of A&E departments nationally, which has now reached 12.5 million consultations annually, reflects shortages in other areas of the service. By not defining what exactly constitutes an "emergency" the Charter has raised patient expectations that cannot be fulfilled. Instead the Government should be clearly saying what they are prepared to pay for. Because people think the emergency service is free, some people call GPs out with less thought than ordering a pizza! The vastly increased demand in this area since the Charter was published has not been matched by either the resources to meet it or the ability of healthcare professionals to ration what they can provide. The brunt is borne by the doctors and nurses who work long shifts and night duties and who often miss meals to deliver this service. They are frequently subject to abuse by patients who believe they have rights but who behave in an irresponsible manner. This happens especially during the long watches of the night, at weekends and Bank Holidays, and seemingly always at the times when the politicians are on their long vacations and the hospital managers are away from their 9-to-5, Monday-to-Friday routines.

3. To be given a clear explanation of any treatment proposed, including any risks and any alternatives, before you decide whether you will agree to the treatment.

4. To be given detailed information on local health services, including quality standards and maximum waiting times.

5. To be guaranteed admission for treatment by a specific date no later than two years from the day when your consultant places you on the waiting list.

6. To have any complaint about NHS services — whoever provides them — investigated and to receive a full and prompt written reply from the chief executive or general manager.

National Standards

The Patient's Charter also contains what it calls "Charter Standards", major and specific standards which the Government looks to the NHS to achieve, as circumstances and resources allow, in, initially, nine key areas. These standards range from excellent, through the obvious, to the totally misguided.

1. Respect. The Charter Standard is that all health services should make provision for proper personal consideration to be shown to you, for example, by ensuring that your privacy, dignity and religious and cultural beliefs are respected. Practical arrangements should include meals to suit all dietary requirements, and private rooms for confidential discussions with relatives.

2. Arrangements to ensure everyone, including people with special needs, can use services.

3. Information to relatives and friends. The Charter Standard is that health authorities should ensure that there are arrangements to inform your relatives and friends about the progress of your treatment, subject, of course, to your wishes.

COMMENT: You should ideally nominate one relative or friend to receive this information, who can then share it with those needing to know. This can relieve the hospital of a time-consuming task.

4. Waiting time for an ambulance service. The Charter Standard is that when you call an emergency ambulance it should arrive within fourteen minutes if you live in an urban area, or nineteen minutes if you live in a rural area.

COMMENT: This is an excellent standard for which to aim. It could easily be met with more careful planning. By my reckoning, 50% of ambulance call-outs are unnecessary and irresponsible and, moreover, an ambulance is often sent when a taxi or ambulance car would be more appropriate.

5. Waiting time for initial assessment in Accident and Emergency departments. The Charter Standard is that you will be seen immediately and your need for treatment assessed.

COMMENT: This is a false standard. The measure that matters is how quickly you are treated and how quickly you are discharged home. The costly exercise of simply having you seen immediately and giving you a category has not meant you are dealt with any quicker − assessment is not treatment. The numbers that nowadays flock to the A&E departments are partly generated by poor access to GP services and partly by a poor understanding of what A&E is for. The excessive numbers, in turn, produce long waiting times which should disappear with a better-informed public and if the Government provide more resources in terms of better access to improved General Practices and extra hospital A&E medical and nursing staff to achieve rapid treatment of more of those patients who should be there.

A&E does not work, and has never worked, on a first come, first served basis. Awarding people categories still means that some are seen more quickly than others. The difference now is that the numbers are greater and people's expectations have been raised, whilst the level of resources has remained the same. It is a sure recipe for conflict and stress.

6. Waiting time in outpatient clinics. The Charter Standard is that you will be given a specific appointment time and seen within thirty minutes of that time.

COMMENT: This looks and sounds impressive but people will only be seen when they can be seen. Besides, the large number of people who currently do not turn up at all, makes a strict appointment system unworkable. Missing a hospital appointment is a very serious issue and a profligate waste of the country's resources and taxpayers' money, yet the Government has not bothered even to mention in the Charter the key responsibility that patients themselves carry in this respect. A patient simply not turning up for an appointment means that someone else has missed out on seeing the consultant at that time, that further time-wasting correspondence is generated between the hospital and that patient's GP and between the GP and patient to arrange another appointment which, in turn, lengthens the waiting list still further.

7. Cancellation of operations. The Charter Standard is that your operation should not be cancelled on the day you are due to arrive in hospital. However, this could happen because of emergencies or staff sickness. If, exceptionally, your operation has to be postponed twice you will be admitted to hospital within one month of the date of the second cancelled operation.

COMMENT: This is a reasonable and humane standard. However, be aware that cancellations can also be caused by the overwhelming demand for beds. The same pool of beds is used for both routine and emergency admissions. Demand is variable. Emergencies, by definition, are random and unpredictable and tend to disrupt the best of schedules.

(Thus for the same reason, the smooth running of the outpatient clinic in most hospitals cannot be guaranteed. Many of the doctors will be part of an on-take team and liable to be called away at a moment's notice to deal with an emergency. This might be, for instance, for an emergency Caesarean section if he is an obstetrician/gynaecologist or, perhaps, to deal with a cardiac arrest if he is a physician.)

8.   A named qualified nurse, midwife or health visitor responsible for each patient. The Charter Standard is that you should have a named qualified nurse, midwife or health visitor who will be responsible for your nursing or midwifery care.

COMMENT: This is a perfectly reasonable attempt to personalise your stay in hospital. However, any nurse into whose care you are assigned, works a 37½−40 hour week. For the remaining 128 hours of that week you will be looked after by the rest of the nursing staff. Again, how personalised your nursing care can be at night, where minimum nurse:patient ratios have not been set and only two nurses may have to look after 38 beds, is not discussed in the Charter. It is a good idea for nurses to wear name badges but, as they are not hotel receptionists, I see no justification for more than the surname to be given; remember, they also have the right to control their relationships with the patients.

But a more important trend is being obscured here. The number of trained nurses is being decreased in our hospitals and their tasks are now allocated to unskilled personnel. Name badges or not, the quality of nursing care is being diminished in our hospitals.

9.   Discharge of patients from hospital. The Charter Standard is that, before you are discharged from hospital, a decision should be made about continuing health or social care needs you may have. Your hospital will agree arrangements for meeting these needs with agencies such as community nursing services and local authority social services departments before you are discharged. You and, with your agreement, your carers will be consulted and informed at all stages.

COMMENT: All discharges should be planned and the resources should be there for you.

The health service belongs to everyone. It is not free. It takes a lot of our nation's resources to run. As citizens we have in the past taken it for granted, almost as a natural adjunct to our lives, something that would always be there for us when we needed it. As life becomes economically tougher in late twentieth century Britain we can no longer rely on the vision that it will always remain the same or deliver the same level of service. We will have to accept more and more responsibility for maintaining our own health. That responsibility will mean keeping ourselves reasonably fit and maintaining a proper diet. It will mean choosing a GP with whom we can work as a knowledgeable partner in maintaining our health. It will mean using the medical services wisely and appropriately. The health service is becoming more open and accountable but at the same time becoming less equal. I hope this book can help you discover where you are likely to get the best treatment so that you will not be among those who lose out. In the next chapter I will consider whether we need to compete for medical services in this way or whether there is a fairer way of organising healthcare — some means whereby everyone gets their fair share of the best treatment available yet which at the same time can keep within the standards of efficiency and value for money that the Government has set.

9.

Where Now?

All of us sometime has had reason to be grateful for the existence of the NHS. If we have had no call for its support in a life-threatening situation, we will know someone close to us who has. The thought of having expert and costly medical intervention available to us should we need it, with no credit checks and no contracts with fine print to worry about, is something to be prized and celebrated.

But two questions need to be asked if we are to have a health service that remains universally popular. The first is: how much as a nation do we wish to spend on health? The second is: how should we ration healthcare to fall within the budgetary limits we have thereby set?

The Government has set its own budgetary limits and has chosen to ration healthcare through the internal market. The theory is that by putting budgets into the hands of GPs it allows them to get the best services for their patients at the lowest price. It introduces choice into the system and at the same time would seem to make it more cost-effective. Yet paradoxically the reverse is happening. The system is becoming more inefficient and choice is beginning to diminish, particularly for those who are not patients of fundholders.

The Internal Market And Its Drawbacks
As I have intimated already, the new internal market in this country is already starting to cause inequality. Those who are registered with a fundholder are sometimes at an advantage. This is not fair in as much as we are all taxpayers and no group of taxpayers should have an advantage over others. Equal access to all the services for GPs is essential and should be based on the clinical need of each patient and not on the funding arrangements, certainly, at any rate in an ideal world.

Of course, these may be only interim inequalities on the road to every GP becoming a fundholder. It remains to be seen if this Government, or any future Government, will have enough money to pay for a full fundholding system or whether the administrative work involved for each GP will cause the system to seize up. If all GPs were fundholders, however, it is unlikely that inequality would disappear, since those in larger practices could wield their greater purchasing power to do better in the marketplace than smaller practices.

Furthermore, the danger of devolving all funding to GPs could be of the large practices essentially dictating the provision of care by the Trusts, putting the small practices at a disadvantage. The healthcare of whole regions could be controlled by a relatively small group of larger practices working together.

A totally free market would, in turn, allow the Trusts to operate on pure commercial lines. There is a possibility that they would concentrate on the profitable services and give undeservedly high discounts and preferences to their larger customers, that is the large group practices, again disadvantaging the small group practice or the single-handed GP. In the absence of any regional planning, the big Trusts could then go on to gobble up the little Trusts by the basic commercial strategy of under-pricing the short-term contract. The little Trusts would go to the wall and services would disappear.

With small competitors out of the way then, just as human nature has shown consistently in the monopolistic practices of big business, the big Trusts could form cartels, indulge in price-fixing and market-rigging and patient choice would be further diminished. The next development might then be a series of Super Trusts running large regional hospitals and knocking out the smaller existing District General type of hospital. This is already starting to happen in some areas. It is the Government's express wish, at the moment, to see Hyper hospitals developed on the "hub and spoke" principle.

In these ways, I fear a loss of local services but the extent to which the "pull" of the internal market — i.e. customer demand — will in practice rule and prevent any damaging changes will be interesting to watch.

As well as the internal market already largely introduced, a newly-devised system of performance related pay is scheduled to come into operation. Theoretically, performance related pay will make people work harder; in reality, I suspect, it may have a negative effect on patient care. If we introduce performance related pay, without appropriate safeguards, doctors will, reasonably enough, want to work mainly in the highly profitable specialities, in high turnover fields of medicine where performance can be measured simply by counting numbers of operations or processes. Few will want to work in the chronic medicine specialities where it is difficult to measure quality. How do you assess the quality of medical or nursing care? These unattractive low profit areas may well become underfunded and understaffed, if offered at all.

Much needs to be done at an early stage to iron out this potential deficiency before it can take hold. Unless it is, there will ultimately be patients who are classified as uneconomic, or shall we say "beyond the interests of the commercial GP or Super Trust". Who are they and what will happen to them? They will be those with chronic illness, low incomes and the aged. We all have a vested interest here because the population is aging all the time. Who is actually going to care for us when we are older? What will happen to each one of us when our personal assets to provide care for ourselves run out? Are we heading for the 21st Century equivalent of the workhouse? These are political questions no Government dare ignore. There are no perfect answers but the public will need to ensure that their MPs know their views.

The Government may simply be forcing those of us with the foresight and the means to plan for our own dotage. If they are, then they should say so, so that we can start to plan at once.

If large groups of taxpayers are eventually to make their own arrangements and reduce the burden on the state by limiting care, then we are still left with the problem of those with no resources of their own. Who will provide care for the elderly, and the chronic mentally and physically ill, and the handicapped? These groups of human beings will clearly be very unattractive to Trusts whose success has to be measured as process completed and income earned. Once again those indefinable qualities of care and compassion will need to be counted and special measures will be necessary to ensure that those unable to look after themselves are not abandoned.

The National Health Service that we have at present still has a dedicated, multi-skilled workforce delivering a reasonably efficient and effective service. The main reasons why we spend so little on our health service and have fewer doctors per head of population compared to other developed countries are the willingness of staff to work long hours and our reliance on overseas doctors. At the moment doctors are not motivated primarily by money. But that could change as Trusts compete with the private sector and set higher salaries for certain specialities.

These changes, along the lines of economic reality, should in theory lead to long term improvements — at least in some eyes — but we will be well-advised to proceed a step at a time, taking care to weed out problems competition cannot solve, or, indeed, which it may cause.

The NHS In Crisis

The NHS now stands at a crossroads. Decisions have to be made. The reforms to date have achieved some valuable advances. There is a recognition that medical resources are not infinite and they have to be managed efficiently so that costs are contained and value for the taxpayers' money increased. There is a recognition, too, that patients must have a say in the way their treatment is conducted. Also the first set of national standards has been published which will help to drive up the quality of patient service.

Nonetheless, the NHS is in a crisis but one that is still largely hidden from the public. There is now an acute and increasing shortage of skilled GPs and hospital doctors. GP training schemes, which, until very recently, used to be oversubscribed, are now no longer having their places filled by home-grown doctors. When they are filled it is often largely by foreign doctors, usually from the EC, who train and then return home. "Where have all the doctors gone?" is a question asked nowadays by every interview panel. The numbers of our brightest students applying to medical school have fallen to an all-time low. One reason is that a career in medicine in the UK is now simply seen as unattractive. The hours are long and the working environment can be harsh. Job satisfaction and youthful idealism wear thin after 56 hours a week non-stop. Doctors are no longer compelled simply by their desire to get it right for humanitarian, moral or intellectual reasons but are now being harried by managers chasing performance targets, and, like many professional groups, are increasingly worried by the risk of complaint or the risk of litigation.

Not only are new doctors not entering the profession but many are taking early retirement and leaving. The rest, whilst perhaps resentful at the growing burden of administration that diverts them from treating patients, are struggling on, because they actually care about their patients and the services they are responsible for, often neglecting their own families and their own health in the process.

The introduction of managers from industry into the NHS has

brought some benefits but it has also brought negative features such as company cars, corporate image, house style, executive suites, secretaries as well as PAs, flash offices, glossy brochures, public relations consultants and, most worrying of all, management consultants supposedly applying their skills used in industry to developing competition between Trusts while in reality charging enormous fees mainly for producing reports scarcely worth the paper on which they are written.

In the three years that followed the start of the NHS reforms, the number of nurses employed fell by 20,000 while the number of managers increased by 16,000 and administrative and clerical staff by 28,000. There is clearly much that is still wrong.

These new managers now inserted into the NHS have signally failed in many areas to redress these skill shortages — surely a management function; many believe they have concentrated on their own empire building and put the needs of the organisation ahead of the needs of the patients. Change, especially of a working culture, takes time so perhaps we must make allowances, but many managers have been imported into the NHS with little acquaintance with the "product" for which they are responsible, in the mistaken belief that management is an abstract process that can be applied mechanically from one field to the next.

However, I have not brought you to this point to fill you full of gloom. Present reality need not be a blueprint for the future. I firmly believe that we still have all the elements in place to run an efficient, cost-effective health service, one that will take care of all the important health needs of the nation well into the next century. It will be rationed but it will be fair and should largely still be free at the point of use for all citizens.

A National Healthcare Strategy
There has always been rationing in the health service. Before the reforms of 1991 people went along with the form of rationing that was then current, most of the time without realising what was happening. We accepted the queues and the waiting lists, the five-minute GP appointment, and the rushed out-patient consultation, only vaguely aware that our access to medical service was, in fact, being curtailed. It was what we were culturally conditioned to expect from a "free" service. Moreover we were probably totally unaware of a tacit agreement between doctors and the state that had existed since the foundation of the health service. Under this

agreement the medical profession enjoyed a large degree of clinical freedom and in return they undertook the unspoken rationing necessary for containing costs. Rationing that could take the form of withholding or postponing treatment − usually on grounds of age.

The advent of fundholding and the creation of hospital Trusts now means that people are becoming conscious that rationing is taking place and that it is not always consistent or fair. The publication of the Patient's Charter, too, has made people aware of basic rights and entitlements and has made them question, too, whether the professionals always know best. They realise, too, that if a doctor is running his own budget he now has a choice; whether to treat them or spend the money on something else. Money saved on prescribing costs can be spent on an extra nurse or a new carpet.

The time is ripe to bring into the open the need for rationing, something that has operated since the NHS began but has never been overtly recognised. As medical technology has made available more treatments than our economy can sustain, it has now become a matter of urgency that we agree on the principle of rationing and its method, on a national basis. Whoever is in power is bound to operate some form of rationing. It is best that the form of rationing is agreed in an open, honest and democratic manner and employed for the greatest good of the greatest number, irrespective of geography or socio-economic status.

My own feeling is that we should simultaneously put the NHS changes on hold, re-examine them and only keep the good bits. Medicine is now audited and analysed; we should subject the management of the NHS to the same scrutiny, evaluating costs, counting the number of tasks done and, above all, measuring the quality of service given. This process should be carried out openly and with the maximum public involvement.

What is needed now is a campaign to educate the public on the issues involved in healthcare and the introduction of mechanisms whereby the public voice can be heard at frequent intervals but divorced from any form of electioneering. The public need to consider how much money should be made available and where it should come from. They need to think about priorities of treatment, about the length of waiting and consultation times, and about what kind of hospitals they want and where they want them.

A Fair Rationing System

Again, we are in the area of necessary future public and political debate. However, it is worth pointing out in this book that there already exist objective yardsticks developed by health economists, in this country and overseas, that can be used to measure the fair allocation of healthcare resources among the population. For the purposes of our national debate, and to take the future of the health service out of the hands of politicians or quangos, the concept of the QALY could be brought forward and explained, and the concepts employed in the groundbreaking Oregon Experiment publicised. A QALY is a Quality Adjusted Life Year, a concept developed by health economists at York University.

QALYs and the Oregon Experiment share the same universalist approach: the common belief that healthcare should be for the greatest good of the greatest number. Applied to healthcare rationing, this means that healthcare budgets should be spent, first, on the interventions that offer the greatest benefit, until all of the benefit has been obtained, then moving on to the second, most beneficial intervention and so on. For example, preventing acute fatality, as in the case of appendicitis or myocarditis (inflammation of the heart muscle) or in the events surrounding childbirth, would be a top priority. Situated near the bottom end of the scale would be procedures such as tattoo removal, reversal of vasectomy and sex change operations. At the very bottom would come treatments for fatal and terminal conditions — where vastly expensive treatments will create minimal or no improvement of the quality of life, for example, treatment of end stage HIV disease and life-support for extremely low birthweight, premature babies (less than 500g).

As in any system, there would be winners and losers, but they would not be for arbitrary reasons. Just as Britain led the way in creating the first universal healthcare programme in the developed world around fifty years ago, so I believe the Government now should allow the taxpaying public the fullest opportunity of being the first country in the developed world to address these issues and make a genuinely democratic decision for the future. It would, no doubt, take an act of great political courage and great trust in the British people to do so. The first step has already been taken in issuing the Patient's Charter.

Having established the public's wishes, the Government needs to create the conditions in which those wishes can be fulfilled. This programme should use taxpayers' money to deliver efficient health services responsive to patients' demands. This would mean that the maximum amount of money goes actually to treating patients, and that resources are provided with priority going to those who actually deliver care, the doctors and nurses and related professions. Whilst accepting the accounting disciplines of business and commerce, strict limits must be applied to irrelevant features such as top-heavy administration, advertising, public relations, and the use of outside management consultants. The task of the reduced number of managers and administrators would be to meet their targets of service delivery to national standards. The task of doctors and nurses would be to spend maximum time treating patients and delivering quality care.

Having defined our targets, we should be able to develop a medical and nursing plan. We will know how many doctors and nurses we will need to deliver the care that the public want. Unfortunately, what will become all too apparent, going on current numbers, is that we will be short of doctors and trained nurses. Equally apparent will be the lack of planned training for doctors and our reliance on overseas graduates of variable skills. A remedy for this will have to be built into the plan.

A stable National Healthcare Strategy would allow us to plan how many surgeons we are going to need and take steps to train them, and also how many other specialists we will need. We simply cannot allow medical training to be as random as it is. The seniors in the medical profession and the Royal Colleges need to review training in management terms in order to stop waste, reduce the repetitive failure rate in the exams and to help us deliver competent, fully trained doctors to the wards, clinics and surgeries of the land to satisfy the need. The doctors that we have now do deliver efficient care but as a nation we could do a lot better. In particular we will need to develop further the role of the GP, which throughout the book has been identified as crucial to your care, and which in the past has been underrated because, historically, hospital medicine has always taken priority. At the moment the Treasury looks on the GP as "gatekeeper" to hospital and other secondary care resources and as a prescriber of expensive medicines. By planning intelligently and openly at a national level we can remove the local rationing role that the GP is being asked more and more to perform, to allow him to be the patient's advocate, a personal doctor who will fight to secure the best medical services, whether it is for an operation to be performed as soon as possible or for the best medicine to treat an illness, regardless of expense.

Likewise Care In The Community, in principle a good approach to caring for the mentally ill, has sadly let down many vulnerable people in our society because of a lack of proper organisation. Staffing and resource levels in this area will almost certainly have to be raised if this scheme is to work properly.

We need to ensure, too, in whatever blueprint emerges, that all those we have trained in our medical schools continue to be able to work for the NHS. We cannot afford the loss from full-time medicine of some of our most talented doctors who, in the present NHS, simply cannot work and have a family life. I refer mostly here to the loss of female skills. Many women doctors are unable to have full time careers because of the way the NHS is organised, representing a waste of investment and a squandering of valuable resources.

But this is only part of a much wider picture of waste and inefficiency which has dogged the NHS since its inception in 1948 and which a sound National Healthcare Strategy could remedy in an innovative way along the lines I am about to propose.

Utilising Present Resources
This proposal would be to utilise fully all the plant and capital equipment at our disposal which we are not doing at present and never have done. In reality, we do not need to build more operating theatres, brain scanners and similar high-cost capital equipment; we just need to employ what we already have at a higher level of use. Industry would not tolerate such equipment standing idle for 128 hours a week, but the health service does. The present NHS is perceived as a 9–5, Monday to Friday operation. It treats routine patients for 40 hours a week and is an emergency-only service for the rest of the time. Scarce and expensive equipment stands idle for long periods.

If I needed something as crucial as a brain scan, I would have no objection to having it at 9pm if it meant getting it carried out quickly and helping expedite any possible treatment I might need.

To do this we need radically to alter the way we run the NHS. My idea is that we run our hospitals on an 0800 to 2200 hours working day, six days a week, so that we operate and scan and use our resources fully for six days per week, 14 hours per day. That is 84 hours per week instead of 40 as at present. Sunday would be a maintenance day.

By running the service further around the clock, we would maximise the use of resources and increase the throughput. Besides allowing women doctors to contribute to the NHS by working flexi-shifts in sensible combinations, it would allow patients to attend at a time more convenient to them. A minor disadvantage is that patients might have to travel to the hospital which has the brain scanner, instead of waiting till one is built at their local hospital. We would also have to reinforce the services in the community to keep up with the greater throughput of the hospitals. Savings made on buildings, theatres and scanners would be available for this purpose.

Also accountancy procedures need to be made uniform in our hospitals. At the moment there are enormous variations between hospitals and between units within hospitals. In figures recently published for one Area Health Authority, there was a variation of cost for the same operation of a magnitude of several hundred per cent! Someone is getting their sums wrong, which prompts the questions: "Are our Trusts financially sound? Have they accurately costed their projects and their liabilities and their equipment replacement budgets? What role do charitable donations and voluntary fundraising play in keeping these hospitals afloat?"

In my view, the case is overwhelming for better utilisation of labour and resources. But "Patients First" must remain the motto, with the public having the right to be consulted about important changes. Above all, when resources are limited, we must eliminate waste by avoiding duplication of equipment, staff and systems. We require careful planning and cost effectiveness. Money should not be squandered on grandiose architectural schemes; buildings need only be functional and comfortable. Nor should money be spent on expensive executive perks, like smart cars and other status-enhancing trappings which are common in big business but out of place in the NHS. Compared to the condition of the wards and doctors' and nurses' facilities, administrative suites in most Trust hospitals can appear positively luxurious.

Help ensure that your local health services are using their funds appropriately. Watch out for fancy seminars in hotels which could have been conducted at little cost in publicly owned facilities. Watch out for excessive use of management and public relations consultants, usually manifested in the publication of expensive literature, glossy brochures and other items of self-publicising window dressing. Question at all times whether your money is going to help frontline staff care for patients or is being diverted elsewhere in the hospital.

The Government and Opposition need to come clean on what must be done with the health service. We need the facts, we need to debate the issues and we need to plan for our own healthcare future, and that of our children and of our children's children. Hidden agendas have no place in a democracy.

Our health is our greatest personal asset; without it we cannot have the good life for which we all strive. But health is not just a question of consulting doctors. It means breathing clean air and having a good diet, a guaranteed supply of water, decent housing and many other things. A good NHS is only one element in staying healthy. We have placed too much reliance on it in the past both as a society and as individuals and we still continue to do so. Why should we as individuals expect the NHS to put right the physical damage of smoking, alcohol abuse, poor diet, lack of exercise and the ravages of time? By examining the way in which health resources should be allocated we will also be examining our own responsibilities towards ourselves and towards each other and how we as a nation and as a community wish to live.

Conclusion

This book has been written in order to promote effective patient power and to provoke debate. Healthcare is probably the most important personal issue for each one of us in the years ahead, far more important than the issues of defence and foreign policy, where vast sums of money are spent. Health is something that really matters to each one of us. In the debate on healthcare, patient power is vitally necessary. We have the right to be consulted about our healthcare future.

The book has also been written to throw some light on more personal aspects of healthcare, to help the reader to understand how to use the NHS to best personal advantage, and to spread the word about our responsibilities to the NHS for which we all pay so much.

This book has not been written to discredit any group or individual. Most of the people who work for the NHS are motivated by a desire to improve patient care. I hope I have taken the good points from the current changes and applied them constructively in my suggestions for the future.

As I have dealt entirely with concepts, no individual is identified, and any similarity to any patient, case, GP practice, hospital or Trust is coincidental.

This book is a simple guidebook. It does not address individual problems but attempts to give the layman the basic facts on the NHS of today. It is not a textbook of medicine, nursing or business management!

However, if it stimulates wide debate involving the patient/ taxpayer, it will have achieved its aim.

APPENDICES

The following reference pages are to help readers find organisations that may be relevant to specific illnesses. Often such groups bring together knowledge unobtainable elsewhere.

They also detail avenues of complaint which may be helpful, including the organisational structures to be found in the National Health Service enabling you to work out who is who and therefore whom to approach. A practice checklist and a GP checklist are enclosed as handy reminders for when you are choosing a new doctor.

Useful Organisations

Action for Victims of Medical Accidents (AVMA)
Bank Chambers
1 London Road
Forest Hill
London SE23 3TP
0181 291 2793

The complaints procedure for medical services; if you believe the clinical care you have received is negligent you should obtain advice and recommendations from AVMA.

Alcohol Concern
Waterbridge House
32-36 London Street
London SE1 0EE

Alzheimer's Disease Society
Gordon House
10 Greencoat Place
London SW1P 1PH

The Anthony Nolan Bone Marrow Trust
The Royal Free Hospital
Hampstead
London NW3 2NT

The Arthritis and Rheumatism Council
Copeman House
St Mary's Court
St Mary's Gate
Chesterfield
Derbyshire S41 7TD

Association for Spina Bifida and Hydrocephalus (ASBAH)
Asbah House
42 Park Road
Peterborough PE1 2UQ

British Colostomy Association
15 Station Road
Reading
Berkshire RG1 1LG

British Diabetic Association
10 Queen Anne Street
London W1M 0BD

British Dyslexia Association
98 London Road
Reading
Berkshire RG1 5AU

British Epilepsy Association
Anstey House
40 Hanover Square
Leeds LS3 1BE

British Kidney Patient Association
Oakhanger Place
Borden
Hampshire GU35 9JZ

Brittle Bone Society
112 City Road
Dundee DD2 2PW

Cancer Care Society (CARE)
21 Zetland Road
Redland
Bristol BS6 7AH

Child Growth Foundation
2 Mayfield Avenue
Chiswick
London W4 1PW

Citizens Advice Bureau
For the address of your nearest Citizens Advice Bureau refer to your
local telephone directory.

Community Health Council (CHC)
An independent body. Represents the interests of the public about
complaints of healthcare. Acts as a 'watchdog' committee. Address
and telephone number obtainable from local telephone directory,
Yellow Pages or FHSA.

Cystic Fibrosis Trust
Alexandra House
5 Blyth Road
Bromley
Kent BR1 3RS

Disabled Living Foundation
380-384 Harrow Road
London W9 2HU

Down's Syndrome Association
155 Mitcham Road
Tooting
London SW17 9PG

Eating Disorders Association
Sackville Place
44 Magdalen Street
Norwich
Norfolk NR3 1JU

Family Health Service Authority (FHSA)
An agency of the NHS. Issues contracts for primary health care to:
General Practitioners, Dentists, Pharmacists and Opticians within a
Health District. Investigates complaints and breaches of service.
Monitors quality of services provided. Address and telephone
number obtainable from local telephone directory or Yellow Pages.

The Foundation for the Study of Infant Deaths
35 Belgrave Square
London SW1X 8QB

The Haemophilia Society
123 Westminster Bridge Road
London SE1 7HR

Helpline (Solicitors)
Write to 'Accident Line'
The Law Society
Freepost
PO Box 61
London NW1 7QS
Telephone Freephone 0500 192939
(This service provides a free half hour interview.)

Hospice Information Service
St Christopher's Hospice
51-59 Lawrie Park Road
Sydenham
London SE26 6DZ

The Ileostomy and Internal Pouch Support Group
PO Box 23
Mansfield
Notts. NG18 4TT

The Kidney Foundation and National Kidney Research Fund
3 Archers Court
Stukeley Road
Huntingdon
Cambs. PE18 6XG

Leukaemia Research Fund
43 Great Ormond Street
London WC1N 3JJ
The fund provides an extensive range of patient information booklets covering the leukaemias, lymphomas, myeloma, aplastic anaemia etc.

London Marriage Guidance
76A New Cavendish Street
London W1M 7LB

Marriage Guidance: see Relate

Multiple Sclerosis Society
25 Effie Road
Fulham
London SW6 1EE

Muscular Dystrophy Group
7-11 Prescott Place
Clapham
London SW4 6BS

The National Association of Laryngectomee Clubs
Ground Floor
6 Rickett Street
Fulham
London SW6 1RU

National Asthma Campaign
Providence House
Providence Place
London N1 0NT

The National Autistic Society
276 Willesden Lane
London NW2 5RB

The National Back Pain Association (NBPA)
16 Elmtree Road
Teddington
Middlesex TW11 8ST

National Eczema Society
4 Tavistock Place
London WC1H 9RA

National Schizophrenia Fellowship
40 Shandwick Place
Edinburgh EH2 4RT

National Waiting List Helpline
St Margaret's House
21 Old Ford House
London EC2 9PL
0181 983 1133

The Psoriasis Association
7 Milton Street
Northampton NN2 7JG

Relate (for marriage guidance)
Herbert Gray College
Little Church Street
Rugby
Warwickshire CV21 3AP

The Samaritans
In your local phone book. Independent and confidential voluntary
organisation befriending and helping the suicidal and despairing. Can
be telephoned 24 hours a day, 365 days a year, during a crisis or
otherwise.

The Samaritans
Head Office
10 The Grove
Slough
Berkshire
01753 532713

The Spastics Society
12 Park Crescent
London W1N 4EQ

Standing Conference on Drug Abuse
Waterbridge House
32-36 Loman Street
London SE1 0EE

The Stroke Association
CHSA House
Whitecross Street
London EC1Y 8JJ

Practice Checklist

1. Is the GP a fundholder?

2. Is it a group practice or single-handed?

3. Do they use a deputising service or do they cover for 'out of hours' themselves?

4. Are telephone contact numbers provided?

5. Does the practice offer evening surgeries?

6. Are Saturday and Bank Holiday emergency surgeries provided?

7. Is there a telephone advice line?

8. Are special clinics provided?
    E.g. well man / well woman / asthma /
          diabetes / hypertension.

9. Are routine clinics available?
    E.g. ante-natal / post-natal / family planning /
          health visitor / children / immunisation /
          cervical smears.

10. What attached facilities are available?
    E.g. psychiatric nurse /
          social worker /
          health visitor /
          midwife /
          physiotherapy /
          chiropody /
          consultant clinics /
          counselling services.

11. What are the standards of cleanliness and decor like?

12. Is there a waiting area?

13. Is confidentiality maintained at the reception desk?

14. Are the staff friendly and helpful?

15. Is there an appointments system?

16. What are the waiting times for routine and emergency appointments?

17. Is there a play area for children and is the practice child-friendly?

18. Is there wheelchair and push-chair access?

19. Is there car parking space? Is this safe and well illuminated?

20. Are there arrangements to provide repeat prescriptions?

21. Is there access to a practice nurse?

22. Are doctors of both sexes available?

GP Checklist

1. Do you like the GP?

2. Do you think the GP likes you?

3. Are you comfortable in his consulting room?

4. Qualifications:-

   MB ChB   These are the basic qualifications
   or MB BS   of Bachelor of Medicine and Surgery

   MRCS LRCP   Basic qualifications

   MRCGP   Member of the Royal College of General
               Practitioners

MRCP   Member of the Royal College of Physicians

MRCPsych.   Member of the Royal College of Psychiatrists

MRCOG   Member of the Royal College of Obstetrics and
              Gynaecology

FRCS   Fellow of the Royal College of Surgeons

Has the GP undertaken Vocational Training in General Practice?

DRCOG   Diploma of the Royal College of Obstetricians
              and Gynaecologists. Such a GP will be
              interested in pregnancy, family planning and
              female problems.

DFFP   (This used to be called the FP Cert.)
              Diploma of Faculty in Family Planning.
              Interested in family planning and sexual health
              matters.

DCH   Diploma in Child Health.

DA   Diploma in Anaesthetics

DipIMC RCSEd
              Diploma in Immediate Care of the Royal
              College of Surgeons Edinburgh

5. A General Practitioner's partner can be a full or part time
    worker.

6. An assistant is a salaried GP.

7. A locum is a medically qualified holiday replacement.

8. Does the GP have a special clinical interest or special skill?

9. What age is the doctor?

10. Which sex is the doctor?

The Primary Healthcare Team

General Practitioner(s)
(They are funded by the FHSA)

```
                          :
                          :
                          :
Health Visitor            :        District Nurse
Practice Nurse            :        District Midwife
                          :
Physiotherapist          :        Social Worker
Chiropodist              :        Community
                          :          Psychiatric Nurse
                          :
```

Practice Manager (Practice Accounts)
   Receptionists
   Secretaries
   Clerical / Filing staff
   Cleaners and Domestics

Consultation Checklist

1. Are you clear in your own mind why you are going to see the doctor?

2. When you are with the doctor describe your problem *and* your worries.

3. Tell your doctor the history of your problem.

4. Answer questions from the doctor about your problem.

5. Be prepared to be examined if necessary.

6. Ask the GP why he is examining you, what his findings are and what they mean. Ask him to explain any tests and test results.

7. Ask the GP what he thinks is wrong and to explain the diagnosis, the treatment, and its effects. What the course of recovery is likely to include and any complications to be expected. Ask when to consult him again, when to return to work and what you can and cannot be expected to do.

8. Before you leave the surgery make sure you understand your problem and the treatment prescribed (if any).

9. Be aware that all you need may be advice, guidance and reassurance.

Summary

Presenting complaint.
▼
History of presenting complaint.
▼
Direct questions.
▼
Examination.
▼
Diagnosis and/or tests.
▼
Treatment.
▼
Follow up and outcome.

In the hospital it will be useful for you to know the medical hierarchy.

The Structure Of A Medical 'Firm' Or Team

Consultant.

Senior Registrar.   (SR)

Registrar.   (REG)

Senior House Officer.   (SHO)

House Officer.   (HO) (Pre-Registration)

All teams should be led by a Consultant with a minimum of a Senior House Officer and House Officer.

Nursing and additional staff on the ward.

The Structure Of A Ward Team

Sister.   (G1) grade.

Sister.   (F)   Physiotherapist.
                                Occupational therapist.

Senior Staff Nurse. (E)   ECG Technician.

Staff Nurse.   (D)   Phlebotomist
                                (blood taker).

Enrolled Nurses.   Ward Clerk.

Student Nurses.

Auxiliary Nurses.   Hotel services.
                                Ancillary staff.

Trust Organisation

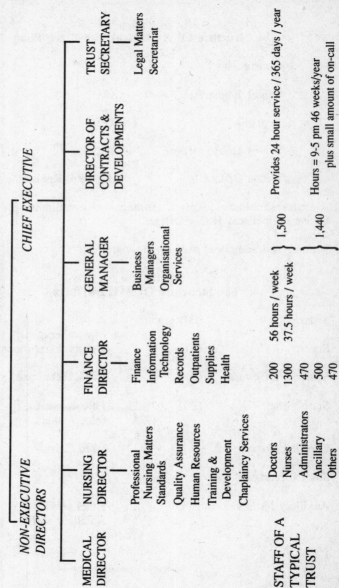

NON-EXECUTIVE
DIRECTORS

CHIEF EXECUTIVE

MEDICAL DIRECTOR	NURSING DIRECTOR	FINANCE DIRECTOR	GENERAL MANAGER	DIRECTOR OF CONTRACTS & DEVELOPMENTS	TRUST SECRETARY
	Professional	Finance	Business		Legal Matters
	Nursing Matters	Information	Managers		Secretariat
	Standards	Technology	Organisational		
	Quality Assurance	Records	Services		
	Human Resources	Outpatients			
	Training &	Supplies			
	Development	Health			
	Chaplaincy Services				

STAFF OF A
TYPICAL
TRUST

Doctors	200	56 hours / week
Nurses	1300	37.5 hours / week
Administrators	470	} 1,500
Ancillary	500	} 1,440
Others	470	

Provides 24 hour service / 365 days / year

Hours = 9-5 pm 46 weeks/year
plus small amount of on-call

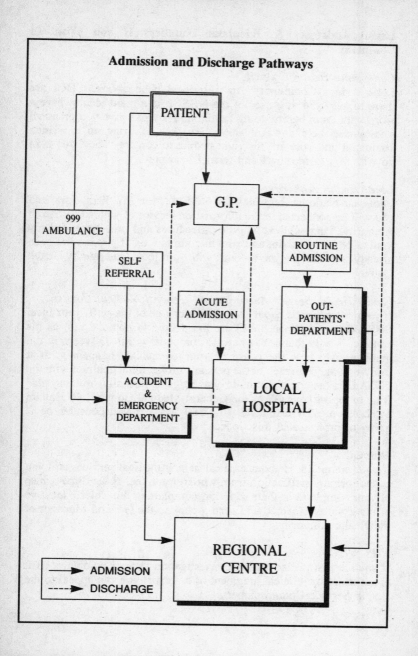

Admission and Discharge Pathways

PATIENT

G.P.

999 AMBULANCE

SELF REFERRAL

ROUTINE ADMISSION

ACUTE ADMISSION

OUT-PATIENTS' DEPARTMENT

ACCIDENT & EMERGENCY DEPARTMENT

LOCAL HOSPITAL

REGIONAL CENTRE

→ ADMISSION

--→ DISCHARGE

Useful Addresses & Telephone Numbers If You Wish To Complain

Community Health Council
Look under "Community" in your local phone book. CHCs are there to help you as a user of the NHS. It is a good idea to have a word with them before doing anything. They can give you practical step-by-step help and guidance, like how to draw up a written complaint and who are the right people to contact. They will even go with you to meetings and formal hearings.

Local Health Authority
Phone the National Helpline 0800 665544 (Mon-Fri, 10am-5pm) and you will be connected to the information service of your local Health Authority. They will explain the procedures and time-limits for any kind of NHS complaint and who to complain to. If you haven't been already, they will put you in touch with your local Community Health Council.

Family Health Service Authority and General Medical Council
If your complaint is about your doctor or one of his staff, your local FHSA (in your phone book) are the people to complain to, as his contract is with them. You have to complain within 13 weeks of the incident, which is the cause of your complaint, happening. If it involves a major breach of the person's professional contract with the FHSA then the complaint will be investigated formally. You may also wish to report your GP to the General Medical Council, 44 Hallam St, London W1N 6AE (Tel. 0171-580 7642) if you consider he is guilty of professional misconduct.

Hospital
If your complaint is about medical or non-medical services and you cannot get any satisfaction from whoever you feel is the direct cause of your complaint or their superior, complain to the Chief Executive of the Trust or Hospital and send a copy to the General Manager of the Health Authority.

NHS Services
If you are dissatisfied with the investigation of your complaint (if it is not about the clinical judgment of a doctor) you can appeal to the Health Service Commissioner:-

Church House, Great Smith St, London SW1P 3BW
Tel. 0171-276 2035 (England)

2nd Floor, 11 Melville Crescent, Edinburgh EH3 7LU
Tel. 0131-225 7465 (Scotland)

4th Floor, Pearl Assurance House, Greyfriars Rd,
Cardiff CF1 3AG Tel. 01222 394621 (Wales)

The Ombudsman, Freepost, Belfast BT1 6BR
Tel. 01232 233821 or 0800 282036 (N. Ireland)

Medical Services and Compensation
If you believe the clinical care you received was negligent and are
looking for compensation, then go to an experienced solicitor. You
can get recommendations and advice from: Action For Victims of
Medical Accidents, Bank Chambers, 1 London Rd, Forest Hill,
London SE23 3TP Tel. 0181-291 2793

Specific Complaints (e.g. Professional Misconduct)
Sometimes these can also be taken further with the following bodies.

For dentists:
General Dental Council
37 Wimpole Street
London W1M 8DQ
0171 486 2171

For nurses, midwives and health visitors:
UK Central Council
23 Portland Place
London W1N 3AF
0171 637 7181

For opticians:
General Optical Council
41 Harley Street
London W1N 2DJ
0171 580 3989

Index

In the same series

100% Fitness

This book will enable anyone, who is interested in improving his or her general fitness, to construct an appropriate programme of activity.

James and Leona Hart describe the basic principles and techniques in the three 'core' training activities of running, circuit training and weight training, and point out how these develop different aspects of fitness. They also give advice on diet and the more common types of sports injuries. The book is ideal for all competitors, joggers, games players and sports enthusiasts.

The Expectant Father

A Practical Guide To Sharing Pregnancy And Childbirth

Betty Parsons has helped many hundreds of husbands and wives to understand pregnancy and labour. She has allayed the phobias, irrational worries and mysteries that have grown up round childbirth. In this book she reaches out to all those who have not benefited from her teaching at first hand, and explains simply but intelligently how a husband can support his wife during this period.

In our Paperfronts series
(Standard paperback size)

The Home Medical Encyclopedia

Gives valuable advice to anyone with an illness in the home, or who wants to understand more about any medical condition.

RIGHT WAY
PUBLISHING POLICY

HOW WE SELECT TITLES

RIGHT WAY consider carefully every deserving manuscript. Where an author is an authority on his subject but an inexperienced writer, we provide first-class editorial help. The standards we set make sure that every **RIGHT WAY** book is practical, easy to understand, concise, informative and delightful to read. Our specialist artists are skilled at creating simple illustrations which augment the text wherever necessary.

CONSISTENT QUALITY

At every reprint our books are updated where appropriate, giving our authors the opportunity to include new information.

FAST DELIVERY

We sell **RIGHT WAY** books to the best bookshops throughout the world. It may be that your bookseller has run out of stock of a particular title. If so, he can order more from us at any time — we have a fine reputation for "same day" despatch, and we supply any order, however small (even a single copy), to any bookseller who has an account with us. We prefer you to buy from your bookseller, as this reminds him of the strong underlying public demand for **RIGHT WAY** books. Readers who live in remote places, or who are housebound, or whose local bookseller is unco-operative, can order direct from us by post.

FREE

If you would like an up-to-date list of all **RIGHT WAY** titles currently available, please send a stamped self-addressed envelope to

ELLIOT RIGHT WAY BOOKS,
KINGSWOOD, SURREY, KT20 6TD, U.K.